The Dinghy Book

The Dinghy Book

SECOND EDITION

Stan Grayson

International Marine Publishing Company
Camden, Maine

Published by International Marine Publishing Company

10   9   8   7   6   5   4   3   2   1

Copyright © 1989 International Marine Publishing Company

Library of Congress Cataloging in Publication Data

Grayson, Stan, 1945–
  The dinghy book / Stan Grayson. — 2nd ed.
    p.   cm.
  Includes index.
  ISBN 0–87742–985–5
  1. Dinghies. I. Title.
VM351.G69 1989   89–1759
623.8′2026—dc19   CIP

International Marine Publishing Company offers software for sale. For information and a catalog, please contact TAB Software Department, Blue Ridge Summit, PA 17294–0850.

Questions regarding the content of this book should be addressed to:

International Marine Publishing Company
Division of TAB Books, Inc.
P.O. Box 220
Camden, ME 04843

Typeset by Farrar Associates, White Horse Beach, MA
Printed by Edwards Brothers, Inc., Lillington, NC
Design by Joyce Weston
Illustrated by Kelly Mulford
Production by Janet Robbins
Edited by J.R. Babb, Jonathan Eaton, Felicity Myers
Photos by author unless otherwise noted.

Contents

Introduction

*T*HIS is a book about the smallest of all small craft, the dinghy or yacht tender, and about what to look for when buying one. Some 10 years have passed since the first edition of *The Dinghy Book* was published. These days, with harbors filled and moorings farther than ever from shore, selecting the right dinghy has assumed even more importance than before. This new edition of *The Dinghy Book* will help you evaluate the available models and make a sound choice.

Primarily, the book is devoted to production dinghies—fiberglass, wood, and inflatable—which are readily available for purchase in marine stores or direct from their builder. In addition, however, there is some discussion of boats that may be built from plans or kits. The market for such craft may be too limited to warrant someone producing them commercially, even in a small way, but they represent an important and viable alternative to production boats, and are included here for those whose specific needs cannot be satisfied by anything else.

Chapter 1 poses five questions crucial to dinghy selection and contains a discussion of each. It is intended to get you thinking objectively and realistically about the factors relating to *you* and your needs. Rarely are one person's needs exactly like another's.

Chapter 2 examines the basic types of rigid dinghy—including flat-bottomed skiffs, round-bottomed dinghies, prams, V-bottomed boats, and traditionally styled small craft—reviewing what each configuration has to offer.

It is all too easy to go to a boatshow, rap one's knuckles against the side of a dinghy, and nod sagely as if one had just discovered something important. Chapter 3 examines construction methods and, more important, details, to help you better evaluate a dinghy and to ask the right questions of its builder. This chapter is central to understanding the strong and weak points of typical small boats.

Chapter 4 covers sailing rigs, oars, and outboard motors.

Chapter 5 is devoted entirely to inflatables. There is no particular reason it is placed fifth in the book, instead of first, for inflatables represent a significant portion of the dinghy marketplace, and for good reason. Inflatables are, if anything, more difficult to evaluate than rigid dinghies, because the materials of which they are made are comparatively esoteric. Before you buy an inflatable, read this chapter.

Chapter 6 discusses dinghies in terms of their use. It is meant to be instructive for the newcomer and thought-provoking for all. Anyone who has been around boats long enough knows someone who might still be alive, had a good dinghy been available at a crucial time.

Chapter 7 offers insights into the business of building dinghies commercially, and includes a descriptive catalog of a wide range of available boats, kits, and plans.

The dynamics of small craft, the various effects caused by different hull forms as they pass through the water, pose problems that can be explained by the formulas and jargon of the naval architect. But this is not a book about naval architecture. It is a book about what you can expect from different sorts of small boats—in terms you can see and feel. Throughout, the effort has been made to demystify small-craft design.

It remains an odd truism that one may spend endless hours of dreaming and planning when purchasing a sailboat or power cruiser, and then buy either the least-expensive or most-available dinghy. Don't let this happen to you! It may be only later that you discover the unsuitability of the boat you have purchased. Often, the discovery is an expensive one.

As we'll see, there is no one answer to any question relating to dinghies, no one dinghy that offers the perfect combination of features to meet everyone's needs. Too often, needs are highly specialized, and local conditions and individual experience play an overriding role. But readers of this book should be in a position to make informed choices and avoid what the venerable E.L. Goodwin of Cape Cod Shipbuilding once observed of dinghy buyers and owners: "People these days," he said, "seem to have the craziest problems with their dinghies."

Stan Grayson
Marblehead, Massachusetts

CHAPTER ONE

So You Plan to Buy a Dinghy!

*Y*OUR dinghy is among the most important, and useful, pieces of gear you will buy. It must, first and foremost, ferry you safely to and from your boat. It will extend the range of your cruising boat, allowing you to explore all manner of coves, creeks, and harbors. It will provide entertainment for you and your children. Someday, it might be called upon to serve as a lifeboat. That is a lot to demand from any boat, let alone one between 7 and 12 feet long, yet some dinghies meet these demands much better than others. There are some very good boats to be bought or built, many more that are acceptable, and a few that are barely passable.

Selecting the right dinghy can be as much fun, or as much trouble, as you care to make it. If you *plan* your small boat purchase, you have the greatest chances for having some fun during the process itself, *and* coming home with a dinghy that will meet your needs. The reverse is also true. Wait until the last minute, and your options (and ultimate satisfaction) are limited. Not long ago, I watched a man leave a boat store with a shiny new dinghy—a boat that was well finished but with improper seat supports, low sides, and poorly placed oarlock sockets. The new owner would not learn about these problems until it was too late.

Even with planning, you may get caught short, as did one sailor I know who found himself rushing around during the week before a planned Fourth of July cruise, desperately searching for an Avon Redcrest and specific equipment at a price he felt was fair. He got the boat, paid top dollar, and lost a day of his cruise in the process. Still, he was ahead of the game, because he had researched his needs and at least knew exactly what boat he wanted, and why.

Helping you reach a satisfactory decision is what this chapter—and this book—is all about. Boating is such a multifaceted activity, and involves learning at least a little about such a wide variety of subjects, that the pitfalls of dinghy evaluation are likely to be learned only by experience. After purchasing a cruising boat and then learning its idiosyncrasies there may be little time left to pay much attention to selecting the boat's tender. Yet it takes little imagination to perceive the dinghy as a great enhancement to the fun offered by the larger vessel, as well as a potential source of danger.

Think fast—which boat has the greater potential to do you in? Your dinghy, as you row out heavily laden in some cold, choppy harbor, or your cruising boat, placidly tugging at her mooring pendant? Clearly, the answer is *your dinghy,* and that is why dinghies must meet stringent Coast Guard loading and flotation requirements. Keep in mind, too, that if your larger boat ever does sink, your dinghy may suddenly be called upon to save your life. This situation falls into the "unthinkable" category, yet boats sink all the time and people must take to their liferafts—or dinghies—most of which were never intended to fulfill such a role.

In fact, the perfect dinghy doesn't exist, and never will. There is only the dinghy that is the best compromise for *you.* Are you a day sailor or weekend sailor or a live-aboard cruiser? Do you sail often on long-distance, bluewater passages or are you a coastwise cruiser? If you are to select a dinghy that best meets your needs, it is important to evaluate these questions candidly. Where can you inspect such boats? Boat shows are the most obvious places. They give you the opportunity to inspect and compare the variety of dinghies typically displayed by boat dealers or by a small-craft builder himself. "Show specials" are often available at a reduced price, and if you know in advance what to look for, you can take advantage of such offers to get the best boat for you at the most favorable cost.

Don't overlook the chance to write for information on boats that interest you, even if they are unavailable in your immediate vicinity. If you are prepared to spend a hefty amount of money for a dinghy with features of particular interest, careful consideration of any available literature and a talk with the builder are well worthwhile.

Most builders like nothing better than the opportunity to talk about their boats. With a few notable exceptions, they are in the business of building and selling dinghies because it is something they really want to do, not because they expect to grow wealthy from their labors. Generally, they are willing to share their ideas and experience with potential customers, and will answer your questions as honestly as they can. Some will make deliveries or arrange for shipment if you are unable to pick up your boat. For builders such as these, you, the customer, become a valuable marketing tool. They know that if you are happy with your boat, you are likely to recommend it to others. And *someone* is always in the market for a new dinghy.

As you begin your search for a dinghy, first answer each of the following questions:

- Where will I keep the dinghy?
- How will I use the dinghy?

- Will outboard power be used?
- Is a rigid dinghy or an inflatable the best choice?
- How much should I pay?

Where Will I Keep the Dinghy?

Not long ago, such a question might not have topped this list—but no more. These days, harbor space is at such a premium that many towns must consider legislation to protect marine-related businesses and prevent further loss of water access from condominium developments. The harbors are overcrowded; there are waiting lists for moorings; and space for dinghies at floats or on racks may be nonexistent or cost more than you wish to pay. Even parking convenient to a place from which you can launch a dinghy is often scarce.

Because of all these reasons, you, like so many other people, may elect to keep your dinghy at home and carry it back and forth each time you expect to use it. At least your boat will be safe from thieves, and it will always be handy for routine maintenance. The drawbacks, of course, are getting to and from your launching site, an operation that can, quite literally, be a drag.

The first requirement, then, is a boat that fits into your vehicle, or one that can *easily* be placed atop it. Remember, too, that the same boat will have to be moved from a parking area to a launching site. Will you be able to carry the dinghy a few hundred yards by yourself, or will you need help? Remember that you might be able to muscle a boat to the water when you're fresh, but getting it back to your vehicle after a tiring day may be another problem entirely.

The answer, for many, will be an inflatable. A high-quality, 8 1/2-foot inflatable dinghy weighs about 45 pounds without floorboards (which you won't want to install every time you use the boat) and often can be carried on one shoulder, leaving the other hand free for oars and a boat bag. The less-expensive inflatable models are likely to weigh the least, and one of these may well suit your needs. When the primary goal is simply getting to your

The dinghy rack. A reasonable way to store a boat. Be sure to lock the dinghy with chain or cable and a rust-resistant lock, and consider a set of transom-mounted wheels or a dolly to help move the boat to and from the water.

Dinghies on the fence. When racks are unavailable and there is no space at the dinghy dock, a chain-link fence can be the homeport for dinghies—given understanding port authorities.

The virtue of light weight. Some boats, like this 7-foot, canvas-covered cedar dinghy once built by the Penn Yan company, can be carried—if you don't have to go too far.

Is there anything more easily stowed than an inflatable dinghy?

boat—never mind in what style—the difficulty of rowing an inflatable against a stiff breeze won't be a major factor. If it is, you'll very likely purchase a small outboard that will *also* have to make the car-to-water trip, and vice versa. Try to be philosophical about such impediments—just one more hurdle to overcome in order to go boating. Nobody said it was easy.

The alternative to an inflatable is a small, rigid dinghy. But as cars have grown smaller, the station wagon capable of carrying the proverbial 4- by 8-foot sheet of plywood or the 4- by 8-foot dinghy made from it has disappeared faster than waterfront property. A few such vehicles are still available to those who need their cargo capacity, and owning one does give you the option of carrying your dinghy inside. Remember, however, that merely *carrying* a 7 1/2- or 8-foot dinghy may be a two-person job, something to keep in mind if you'll be sailing much by yourself. At the expense of added complication and cost, it might be worth buying or building a small dolly that mounts on the transom or in the daggerboard trunk.

If the dinghy is to be left *on* a float, the flexibility in choice increases dramatically. Now, you are limited only by the size of boat that can be comfortably launched on your own and, perhaps, by the dinghy's gunwale construction. Boats with gunwales formed by a flange are more susceptible to damage from frequent rolling over on shore than are boats with wooden gunwales, as Chapter 3 makes clear. If you're reasonably gentle, however, a flanged gunwale can survive quite a lot of rolling over—thus opening up a great variety of reasonably priced boats from which to choose.

The rooftop carrier. Be sure the boat is protected from chafe. Beamy dinghies may require custom racks, which can be made of wood and fitted to the vehicle's built-in roofrack. You can save time by making up special lengths of line with which to lash the boat forward, aft, and to the rack.

These wheels may be removed from the transom when not in use. Dual wheels, or wheels with wide tires, provide added "flotation" in sand.

Permanently attached wheels mean one less thing to lose. Note the useful sculling notch.

The most convenient place to keep your dinghy is *in* the water, either at a dinghy float or on a pull-line. The float is the most common method. Its disadvantage is that your boat (which should be secured with chain and a rust-resistant, solid-brass lock!) is sharing space with many other little boats, all jostling, banging, and thumping into one another. Hard knocks are a fact

The dinghy float. The most convenient place to leave your dinghy is in the water, but dinghy docks subject boats to a lot of jostling. A good rubrail and fenders are necessary. These sturdy prams have a number of desirable features: two sets of oarlock sockets to permit good weight distribution, reinforcing quarter knees forward and aft, and a center support for the thwart.

One solution to security. The same chain that secures the dinghy passes through holes in the oar blades.

The pull-line. An ideal way to moor a dinghy when security is not a problem. Be sure to remove oars and oarlocks, and paint or otherwise identify the boat in more than one location.

of life at the dinghy dock, and good rubrails and strategically placed fenders are required if your boat is to maintain its looks. You can always leave an inflatable at the float, of course, but while they don't get nicked and gouged as a rigid dinghy does, they do occasionally become chafed, and inevitably begin to fade under the relentless assault of ultraviolet rays. Unless their bottoms have been properly coated, they quickly become foul, and scraping an inflatable's bottom involves some obvious risks.

The pull-line represents another alternative, and if you find room for one and believe theft is not a major threat, there is much to recommend it. Your boat essentially will be moored out on its own, yet will be readily retrievable. Even if you're not concerned about theft, always take oars and oarlocks home with you. Remember to bring a bailer if your boat has no cover.

How Will I Use the Dinghy?

Because many of the best books that include advice about dinghies are written by long-term cruisers, that advice is written from a very specific viewpoint. The prudent seaman considers whether he can row his dinghy and an anchor to windward on a dark and stormy night, and whether he can repair it easily in a remote harbor.

The great majority of dinghies, however, are not bought by world cruisers, but by weekend sailors whose needs are quite different. Is rowing a practical

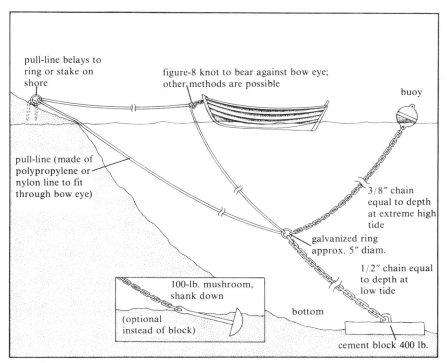

pull-line belays to
ring or stake on
shore

figure-8 knot to bear against bow eye;
other methods are possible

buoy

pull-line (made of
polypropylene or
nylon line to fit
through bow eye)

3/8" chain
equal to depth
at extreme high
tide

galvanized ring
approx. 5" diam.

1/2" chain equal
to depth at
low tide

100-lb. mushroom,
shank down

(optional
instead of block)

bottom

cement block 400 lb.

*The ultimate dinghy pull-line. These specifications can be scaled down in
protected waters.*

alternative to motoring for you? If it is, and particularly if you are buying an
8-foot or larger boat, then soft-chine models will be worth investigating. So
will flat-bottomed skiffs or prams with properly rockered bottoms, many of
which row surprisingly well.

If your boat is moored in a swift current or a long way from shore or you
just don't like to row, then you'll want to inspect boats designed expressly for
motoring, such as the Boston Whaler and catamaran-type designs.

What about sailing performance? Because none of these boats is intended
for much more than playful relaxation under sail, assess how easy the boat is
to rig. You want something simple and quick, with spars no longer than the
hull. If frostbite or another sort of dinghy racing is popular in your area and
you want to participate, then perhaps that factor will strongly influence your
selection.

Don't rule out traditional-style rigs such as lugsails and spritsails because
you have had no experience with them. Such traditional rigs can have a

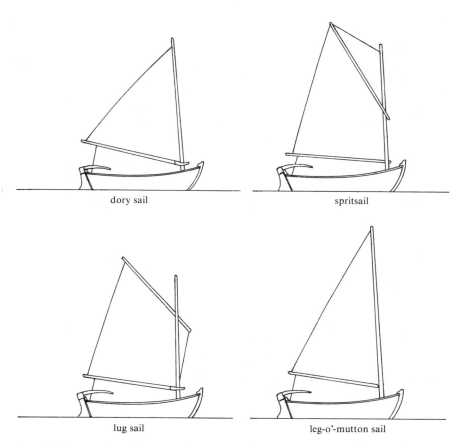

dory sail   spritsail

lug sail   leg-o'-mutton sail

Alternative rigs for a sailing pram, sketched by designer Fenwick Williams. The booms of all but the spritsail are cocked upward to give more headroom in the little boat. The lug rig permits a comparatively large yet low sail, which offers good drive with a short mast.

comparatively large yet low sail that offers good performance while minimizing the risk of capsize. But whatever the rig type, try to sail the boat before you buy it. Performance may, or *may not,* be acceptable, particularly if the rig is loose-footed. Chapter 4 discusses aspects of dinghy rigs in detail.

Is It Likely Outboard Power Will Be Used?

This is an important question, even for those who believe they don't like outboards and wouldn't have one. I will long remember the night when the

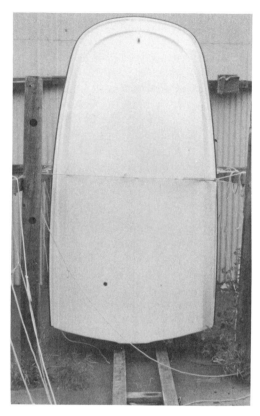

A bottom designed for outboard power. The broad, flat after surfaces of this hard-chine Boston Whaler will support the weight of outboard and crew and make the most of the outboard's performance potential.

questionable virtue of an oars-only policy was brought home to me and a sailing pal proud of his new 8-foot, soft-chine dinghy. Equipped with a pair of well-leathered 7-foot oars, the boat was a dream to row. It almost felt as though we were in a dream, too, as we pushed off at midnight against a stiff breeze and a chop, rowing to his boat, moored somewhere in a strange harbor. With the two of us and our gear aboard, the heavily laden dinghy rowed marginally in those conditions. After 15 minutes of *hard* pulling, my friend turned the oars over to me; it was 15 minutes more before we identified his boat's dim silhouette, and we had spent several of those minutes resting, gratefully holding onto a moored boat in our path. It was only after we got aboard that we discovered we had no flashlight to shine at the combination lock. . . .

If your boat is moored some distance from shore and you are unable to buy at least a 9-foot dinghy designed for good rowing performance, an outboard motor will likely be a practical investment. It wasn't long before a 2 hp motor was clamped to the stern of the boat in question. Because its bottom was reasonably flat in the aft portions, the boat handled the outboard well. So, if you are a weekend sailor who regularly must row a long distance, a blue-water cruiser who is likely to have a long pull in from remote anchorages, or if you must contend regularly with a strong current, seriously consider purchasing an outboard.

Is a Rigid Dinghy or an Inflatable the Best Choice?

The comparative advantages and disadvantages of inflatables (see Chapter 5) versus hard dinghies have been widely debated, but it's like comparing apples and oranges: each type has much to offer and the decision about which one to purchase can only be based on your own personal situation.

Some of the inflatable's advantages, its portability and light weight, have already been touched upon. These alone will be the overriding factors for many people in their purchase decision. The trade-off is rowing performance and durability. Wind is the chief enemy of the oar-powered inflatable, but the fair-weather sailor who is able to choose his sailing days may be unaffected. In protected water, in light breezes, a good inflatable can actually be pleasant to row, performing as well as some small rigid dinghies—if you are alone and the boat is equipped with floorboards. When conditions are poor, however, an inflatable with floorboards and a reliable outboard might be preferable to a hard dinghy that rows well.

Even the best inflatables won't stand up to rocky beaches or coral as well as a hard dinghy will. Those who frequent such areas will find the inflatable no bargain. Its service life will be shortened, and, because good inflatables are not cheap, the need to replace the dinghy within a relatively short time must be considered. Sand, too, is capable of grinding away fabric and coating, especially where the floor joins the buoyancy chambers. On the other hand, for the weekend cruiser, a good inflatable, well cared-for, may well last for five to 10 years or more. And less-expensive models are available at prices that make it practical to purchase a replacement every few years.

High-quality inflatable dinghies offer great stability. They are hard to capsize—an important consideration for those carrying kids or guests who aren't sailors themselves. They also offer some degree of "liferaft" potential. Full-time cruisers may well solve the hard-versus-soft-dinghy question by carrying one of each. Chapter 5 is devoted entirely to inflatables and what to look for in selecting one.

How Much Should I Pay?

Serviceable 8-foot fiberglass dinghies typically have list prices of about $550 to $650, with a 7 1/2- to 8-foot wooden-gunwale boat typically in the $700-plus region. Yet, such a boat can also cost $1,500 or more. The price range of inflatables is at least equally dramatic, with 8-footers available at less than $200 to about $1,000, although options such as floorboards, motor mounts, and dodgers can increase the list price. Large marine discount houses often carry a few inflatables in their catalogs, including top-quality models, and that gives buyers a choice that seldom exists with the more expensive fiberglass dinghies.

Leaving aside the question of personal finances, there remains the question of how much you *need* to pay to acquire a dinghy that will meet your requirements. With dinghies—just as with cars, cameras, and most anything else—there comes a point of diminishing return. Just as a Ford or Chevrolet will convey you to work as effectively as a Cadillac or Mercedes-Benz, a $500 8-foot dinghy will get you to your boat about as well as a $1,500 8-foot dinghy. The less-expensive boats can even be found rendering faithful service years after their purchase, although they may well have needed some structural beefing-up along the way.

Will the $1,500 boat last three times as long or perform three times as well as the $500 model? It won't. But its typically stronger construction, better finish, and possibly better design may be worth paying for if you are a serious cruiser. Generally speaking, I recommend buying the best boat you can afford, while noting that the great majority of buyers probably do not need the most expensive model. But keep in mind that a rigid dinghy or, particularly, an inflatable, *may* someday be called upon to save you if your boat ever sinks. If that happens, the price difference between (to take just one example) an inflatable dinghy with the highest-quality fabric and sturdiest oarlocks and a flimsier model may seem very small indeed.

Increasingly, nowadays, the dinghy's role is changing. As harbors become more crowded and moorings are set ever farther from shore in relatively exposed areas, there is clearly a need for a seaworthy dinghy that performs well with an outboard. In areas where marinas or other docking arrangements are prevalent—or for those who cruise from one slip to another—a dinghy may not strictly be *needed* at all. For them, the dinghy may serve only occasionally, and, even then, may be thought of as a lifeboat or as entertainment. But for these boaters, too, the five basic questions still apply. Once you have some general answers to them, once you have decided generally on the type of boat you need, you are ready to get into the specifics of design and construction—the subjects of the next two chapters.

Parting Shots

- Be pragmatic when assessing your dinghy purchase. Base your plans on where you'll be keeping the boat and how you will use it. If you are a weekend sailor, you probably don't need a dinghy designed for long-distance cruisers or live-aboards.

- Do not get caught up in the "which is better" argument involving rigid dinghies versus inflatables. Each will answer different people's needs. Occasionally, it makes sense to own *both*.

- Do not underestimate the value of a small outboard or reject outboards because they offend your "purist" sensibility. Many dinghy owners find an outboard adds immensely to the usefulness of their boats. Do compare at least a couple of different outboards before you buy.

- Keep an open mind about price when buying a dinghy. You may not need the most expensive boat, but you also may regret making a selection based on what costs the least. Look for value and performance, and balance those features against the price.

CHAPTER TWO

Design Types
and Performance

A LMOST every month, the pages of yachting magazines present the plans for, or pictures of, a new dinghy. Each year, small companies are formed to produce such boats and each year, such companies also go out of business. While it's difficult to make a living building and selling small boats, these periodic comings-and-goings have little effect on dinghy development. The new boats keep appearing, and the boating public reaps the rewards—there is a dinghy for every budget. If a particular boat proves a disappointment for one reason or another, you can always sell it—for someone is always looking for a bargain in a used dinghy—and try something else. But which one? Why are there so many decidedly different approaches to the same basic problem?

Although the average yacht chandlery or boat dealer may handle one or two lines of dinghies, it will quickly become apparent to even the casual shopper that the range of types is enormous. However, the claims made for each of these little boats are, for the most part, similar. Brochures talk of rowing, towing, sailing, and motoring performance all wrapped up in their particular dinghy package. These are all desirable attributes, but they also happen to be mutually exclusive. No one boat will do them all. But, after all, you are not looking for rowing-shell performance in your dinghy or the sailing ability of a one-design; you're looking for a good compromise. On the other hand, if you have no intention of powering your dinghy with an outboard, you may well want to select a boat designed primarily for rowing performance.

Once you cut through all the hype about "classic design" and the promise of great *all-around performance,* you find yourself looking at pictures of a lot of little boats with one or another of three basic design features: (1) the type of bottom: flat, V-shaped or round; (2) the shape of the bow (most dinghies have a pointy bow, although some are pram types, with snub noses); and (3) the size, which relates with equal and great importance to all the boats, no matter what the configurations of their bottoms or the shapes of their bows.

This chapter will examine the typical design features and performance aspects of each dinghy type. As you read, remember that the design of any small craft involves a number of interrelated variables. One cannot think of a boat's carrying capacity merely in terms of how wide or long it is. Its freeboard is important, too, as are the shape of its sides and the length of its waterline. These may not be the sorts of things you'll think about as you're rowing out to your mooring, but they are precisely the things that will determine whether or not the dinghy you choose will satisfy your individual boating needs.

Below is a list of terms typically used in dinghy advertising and design articles.

A Small Boat Vocabulary

Beam   a boat's width at its widest point. Most practical dinghies are about 4 feet or more in beam, no matter what their length. Anything narrower, while possessing somewhat improved rowing or sailing performance, is likely to be too tender (tippy) for comfortable use as a yacht tender.

Broadstrake   the middle strake or plank in the hull of a lapstrake wooden boat with three planks on each side.

Carvel   a type of wooden hull that is smooth-sided, built of strips of wood fastened and glued together or with flush-fitting planks with caulked seams. The method is not particularly practical for dinghies unless they remain in the water, thus preventing the seams from drying out and leaking when the boat is relaunched.

Chine   the lower edge of a boat's hull where it joins the bottom. Flat- or V-bottomed boats, in which the bottom forms an abrupt angle to the sides, are known as "hard-chine" designs. Round-bottomed boats are "soft-chine" designs.

Deadrise   the degree of curve or the angle formed by the boat's bottom from keel to chine. A flat-bottomed boat thus has no deadrise.

Depth   the straight-line distance from the top of the gunwale to the lowest point in the hull. Depth relates especially to carrying capacity; the greater the depth, the greater the volume of space available within the hull.

Flare   the angle off the perpendicular of a hull's sides. A boat with vertical sides would have no flare at all. Generally, flare adds stability as a boat tips or heels over in the water, and it enhances "dryness" by reducing somewhat the amount of spray cast into the boat.

Freeboard   the distance between the gunwale and the water. Even when fully loaded, a dinghy should have adequate freeboard to avoid being swamped by the chop that can normally build up in a harbor.

Garboardstrake   the plank immediately adjacent to the keel on a wooden boat.

Gunwale   the upper edge of the hull. The two major gunwale types on fiberglass dinghies are "flanged" and wooden. Both are discussed in Chapter 3.

Lapstrake　also known as "clinker," this construction method features overlapping wooden planks that require no caulking. The result is a sturdy boat generally lighter in weight than a carvel-planked type. The laps add somewhat to the boat's stability, and fiberglass dinghies occasionally are molded with "lapstrakes."

Rocker　the curve in a boat's bottom when viewed from the side, like the curved runners of a rocking chair. A rockered bottom typically places a portion of both bow and stern out of the water to minimize resistance and increase buoyancy as the boat is loaded and sinks lower in the water.

Sheer　the sweep of the gunwale from bow to stern.

Run　the portion of the boat's bottom from about amidships to the stern.

Sheerstrake　the topmost strake or plank in the hull of a lapstrake boat.

Skeg　the area of a keel that runs aft to the transom. The absence of a skeg, or the presence of a skeg that is too small, can result in a boat that shears off to one side or another when being towed.

Stem　the very forwardmost part of the bow. Most dinghy stems are cut back beneath the waterline to enhance the boat's maneuverability. Pointed-bow dinghies are sometimes referred to as "stem dinghies."

Thwarts　the boat's seats. Most run across the dinghy from one side to the other, "athwartships." Some thwarts are positioned fore-and-aft, permitting the rower's weight to be shifted depending on how the dinghy is loaded. The height relationship of the thwart to the gunwale has an important effect on how a boat rows.

Size — The Critical Factor

All of the complexly interrelated variables of a boat's performance—its stability, buoyancy, righting ability, and carrying capacity—are related to its size. Given the small size of most dinghies, 6 1/2 to 12 feet, even a slight increase or decrease in size will have a dramatic effect on a boat's design and performance. Going from an 8-foot to a 10-foot dinghy, while increasing all other dimensions proportionately, would slightly more than double the boat's stability, internal capacity, and buoyancy.

What that means to you is fewer trips to and from the dock, and a comparatively dry boat with extra ability to rise with the waves. What that means to a designer is the chance to avoid overly full lines if he's drawing a soft-chine dinghy. As length increases, beam can be reduced somewhat in proportion to length, and the formerly quite full curves of the bottom can be refined, making the boat more "seakindly" and permitting it to slip easily through the water. Finally, as the boat increases to 11 or 12 feet, about the maximum size for a yacht tender, the designer can configure the shape to

Generous beam and firm bilges. This round-bottomed Oxford Dinghy shows the stability possible in a soft-chine boat of good design.

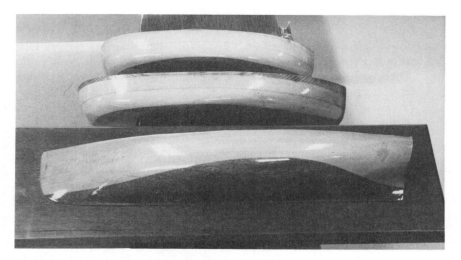

Slender and tubby. These half models illustrate the fuller lines necessary as a dinghy diminishes in size from 12 feet to 10 feet to 8 feet.

achieve some real rowing and sailing performance, rather than merely seeking to maximize carrying capacity and stability.

It is for these reasons, then, that the smaller the dinghy, the more likely it is to be full-lined and plump rather than fine-lined and sleek, and to have a flat or V-bottom with little deadrise rather than the gracefully curved bottom of a larger boat. The accompanying illustration shows how a soft-chine dinghy must become fuller as it becomes smaller in order to maintain adequate weight-carrying capacity and stability.

A Famous Yacht Designer Talks About Dinghies

"A good tender is one of the most difficult things to design, for it must possess several features which are somewhat conflicting. If she is light, she is easy to haul on deck, but quick moving underneath you until you are seated. The light boat is also generally more easily damaged. If her freeboard is high she will be drier and perhaps abler, but she will stick up high on deck and interfere with the vision of the helmsman. If a tender has a straight run and a large stern, she will go well with an outboard motor, but will be very hard to row when fully loaded. The large stern and straight run will also make her extremely difficult to tow, for in a following sea she will run up on her painter and yaw off in first one direction and then the other, while the tender with just the right turn-up aft will hold back in place and keep her painter tight. . . ."

—L. Francis Herreshoff,
Sensible Cruising Designs

The Basic Flat-Bottomed Skiff

One day, while picking my way along the rocky fringes of Marblehead Harbor, I stopped to examine a number of dinghies used by local fishermen. These boats, by and large, are a rough-looking lot used to ferry working gear back and forth to lobsterboats. They have one overriding element in common: The great majority are wooden, flat-bottomed skiffs or prams.

Why flat bottoms? They're inexpensive by comparison with round-bottomed boats, they are stable, and they are sturdy. The basic skiff built out of pine or cedar can take a lot of hard knocks. With care, such boats can remain serviceable for 50 years and more. Skiffs built of good-quality plywood also combine toughness with the potential for long life. With these desirable features, why has the flat-bottomed dinghy been ignored by so many recreational sailors? Perhaps it seems too humble a craft to merit consideration. Then, too, production dinghies are usually fiberglass, and flat expanses of fiberglass would need to be either quite thick and heavy or else well braced if they are to be durable.

As much as the working waterman, the recreational sailor can benefit from the flat-bottomed dinghy's stability. It's reasonably easy to get into and out of, especially if you remember to step about in its middle (a basic safety concept when entering or exiting any small craft). It's not so tippy that it will frighten uninitiated guests, either. Although a lobsterman may not need to be concerned with towing his dinghy, a well-designed skiff can tow very well. Their flat bottoms and shallow draft also permit them to creep right through shallow water to the beach.

As with anything else, there are both good and not-so-good examples of the basic flat-bottomed skiff. Among the features to be avoided are perfectly straight sides, a comparatively narrow beam, little or no sheer, and a bottom with little or no rocker. Naval architect John Atkin is among the few designers today who have adapted the flat-bottomed skiff for serious use as a yacht tender. His criteria for a good boat include a fine entrance; just the right amount of rocker; a fine, pulled-in stern; and lots of flare. The flare adds lift as the boat rides through the water, and deflects spray. By contrast, a slab-sided, vertical bow would tend to go into the seas rather than lift over them.

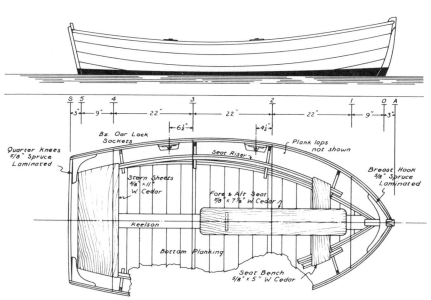

Two flat-bottomed dinghies designed by John Atkin—Cabin Boy *(above) and* Tri-trainer *(right).* Cabin-Boy *is a sturdy 7 1/2-footer with a longitudinal thwart that permits the rower to best distribute his weight using one of two sets of oarlocks. The* Tri-trainer *was designed to instruct youngsters in all phases of small-boat handling and could serve as a tender to larger boats. Note the spacing of the oarlocks 8 inches aft of the thwarts. (Such measurements are discussed in detail in Chapter 3.) The boat's hull is built of two 4-foot-by-12-foot sheets of 1/4-inch marine plywood.*

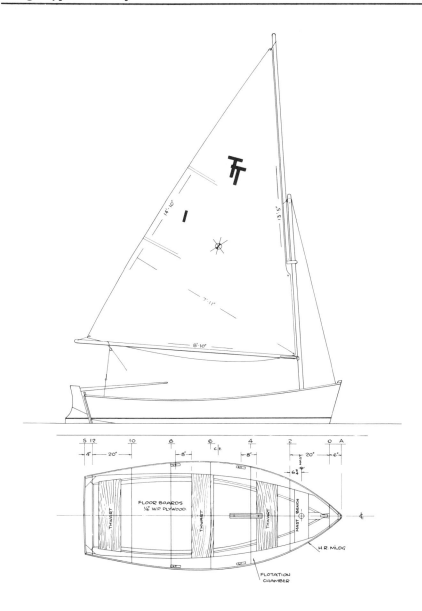

Rocker

A well-designed flat-bottomed skiff—like one of Atkin's boats or the craft designed a century ago by New Bedford (Massachusetts) builder Asa Thomson—has a certain amount of rocker to its bottom. Typically, the rocker

An elegant flat-bottomed tender. This skiff was built from a design by nineteenth-century New Bedford boatbuilder Asa Thomson. Neither slab-sided nor heavy for its length, it combines usefulness, good performance, and good looks. Plans for the boat are available from WoodenBoat *magazine.*

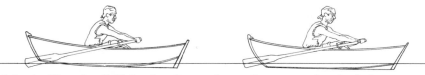

A boat with rocker (left) has less drag and more buoyancy when loaded. Inadequate rocker (right) incurs drag when rowing, particularly when the boat is loaded.

A pram designed by Fenwick Williams. Note the well-rockered bottom that adds buoyancy to the boat's ends and enhances rowing performance.

The original Westport Skiff was created in Westport, Massachusetts by boatbuilder Fred Tripp and owned for a time by designer/builder/historian Robert H. Baker. It was Baker who eventually took off the little boat's lines when, through some neglect, she gave up after more than three decades of service.

Does such a boat have potential as a tender? That depends. She'll never be an all-around performer in the manner of a simple but well-designed plywood pram. But, if you'll use the skiff mostly as transportation to and from your boat; if you'll keep her on a pull line and need to bring her right onto the beach so you can step in with dry feet (the bottom has three rubbing strakes for protection); if you recognize that she's low-sided and so best suited for calmer water; and if you want to try your hand at building a simple, sturdy boat that will stand up to plenty of rough use . . . yes!

I wouldn't plan on towing this skiff; but if you keep a small inflatable aboard for your cruising, you won't need to. Use her as a back-and-forth workhorse; Baker said the boat rowed well unless her rockered stern, which makes her unsuitable for an outboard, was heavily loaded.

The skiff has two rowing stations for balance and a short foredeck to keep things dry. She won't perform as well as the flat-bottomed but more elegant Asa Thomson skiff pictured earlier, but she's an evocative, traditional small craft that's much easier and less costly to build. A story about the skiff appeared in WoodenBoat, *Number 32, and plans may be ordered from Baker Boatworks (address in Chapter 7).*

will raise the transom free of the water, reducing drag for a solo rower and adding buoyancy as the stern sinks lower under the weight of a passenger. At the bow, rocker will be less, reducing drag when the boat is lightly loaded but enhancing buoyancy as weight is added toward the bow.

If rocker is a good thing, too much of it can result in peculiar, if not downright dangerous, handling. Excessive rocker could cause the boat to hobbyhorse (up and down) at each oar stroke, or perhaps even go out of control or flip over backward if too much outboard power is applied. Once, to investigate this matter of how much rocker was too much, designer Fenwick Williams developed a pram with pronounced rocker. This little boat performed very well, at least under oars. But, as the designer pointed out, anything more than the tiniest outboard could easily make such a boat dangerous.

The Skeg

If rocker is critical to rowing performance, so is the skeg. It is essential that the skeg be adequately proportioned so the skiff will track in a straight line. Most designers believe that the larger and longer the skeg, within reason, the better. A large skeg also adds lateral resistance when a dinghy is rigged as a sailboat, and it helps any dinghy tow in a straight line—obviously a desirable trait. Few sailboats are designed to accommodate the dinghy on deck, and a dinghy that tows docilely minimizes drag and strain on towing gear and fittings.

The Skegless Skiffs of Martha's Vineyard

Having noted the general goodness of skegs, I should mention that the skiffs used by fishermen on Martha's Vineyard traditionally were built with no skeg at all. There was a good reason for this. The boats were routinely launched from the beach, and a skeg tends to dig into the sand during launching. These boats were *not* known for their towing qualities, which were particularly poor in a following sea. But in addition to being easy to launch and retrieve, the skiffs were stable—11 footers capable of carrying two people, eight bushels of oysters, a culling board, dredges, and an outboard, albeit with admittedly marginal freeboard.

The Hard-Chine Hull

What about the rowing performance of a hard-chine dinghy? In theory, any hard-chine hull produces more eddies and drag as it moves through the water than a round-bottomed boat. In reality, however, such considerations are often outweighed by the benefits of a flat-bottomed boat. For one thing, in the very smallest sizes, only a hard-chine boat offers the necessary stability. For another, the stability of these boats—and, for home builders, their comparative simplicity—is likely to outweigh any rowing performance advantage a round-bottomed type may have. As always, much depends on the individual needs and preferences of the boat's owner.

Too few good flat-bottomed dinghies are available on a production basis. If you are particularly interested in one, you will find more information about them in Chapter 7. If you decide you want a flat-bottomed skiff, you will probably have to build it yourself or buy a boat from one of the few companies, such as Lowell's Boat Shop (see Chapter 7), that does offer them.

But, should you elect to undertake the enriching experience of building a small boat for yourself, you could do a lot worse than a flat-bottomed skiff.

The Flat-Bottomed Pram

A dinghy becomes a pram when its bow, instead of curving to a point at the stem, is shaped to form a "transom" rather like the one at the boat's stern. There is a very good reason for doing this: Particularly on very small dinghies, the pram bow permits added weight-carrying volume. Essentially, prams are small boxes with big dimensions. Their shape makes them a natural for amateur construction and in addition to their many other virtues, many prams can be built inexpensively and with a modest number of tools.

While their blunt bows might suggest that performance must suffer by comparison to a pointed-bow boat, prams can, in fact, offer excellent performance. Yacht designer L. Francis Herreshoff even believed prams were "the best model for a small tender." Prams of his design, or inspired by his work, are available today from a number of custom, small-craft builders.

As important as rocker is to a flat-bottomed skiff, it is also vital to a flat-bottomed pram, and it can, in fact, be the difference between a good-performing boat and a dog. When lightly loaded, a properly rockered pram

A pram by Lowell's Boat Shop. Prams offer the most capacity in the smallest package. The bow transom does offer more resistance to wind and seas than a curved stem, but when the boat has adequate rocker, or the dainty bow transom of some prams built to Scandinavian lines, the trade-off is usually modest.

has both the bow and stern transoms raised above the waterline (this also positions the bow eye at just the right height for towing). As weight is added, the ends of the boat will sink lower in the water, and resistance will increase, but the boat then will be carrying a surprisingly heavy load for her size. On a pram with insufficient rocker, the bow transom would form a bluff wall impeding easy passage through the water, while the stern would drag, further retarding progress.

When it comes to load-carrying ability, flare in the topsides works together with the boat's rocker. A tiny 6-foot 8-inch pram designed by Bill Peterson has carried in excess of 750 pounds, thanks in part to the rake of the transoms and the flare of the sides.

The real beauty of small craft like these becomes apparent when you consider the deck space available for dinghy stowage aboard most cruising boats. After studying the kinds of boats owned by most people, designer Bill Peterson became convinced that few had enough deck space to stow even a 7-footer. The 6-foot 8-inch pram was the smallest dinghy he found practical. He wanted to keep the weight to 75 pounds—just about the maximum one person can lift

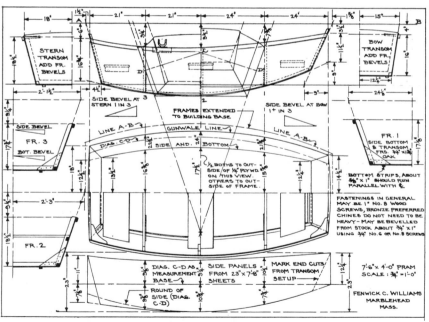

The beauty of flat-bottomed boats. Comparatively easy construction is one advantage of a flat-bottomed boat like the Williams pram. When well-designed, as this pram is, stability and performance are also excellent.

and carry—and another foot of length would have increased the weight to 100 pounds.

The pram's simple shape also makes it ideal for construction as a nesting dinghy. Production versions of such prams are available, as well as plans for several more, including the 7-foot 10-inch Eric Sponberg–designed Halfling. When stowed, this dinghy occupies a space of 48 inches by 54 inches by 20 inches, and each section weighs only about 30 pounds.

If prams offer good load-carrying capacity for their compact overall dimensions, they also are weight-efficient. Weight is a concern for almost anyone who must launch or carry a dinghy. Light weight may also be important to owners of multihull yachts who wish to keep weight down for performance reasons. The 7-foot 10-inch Uqbar dinghy, for example, designed for plywood construction, weighs 55 pounds. A well-built fiberglass dinghy of that length might *easily* weigh 40 or 50 pounds more.

In relatively calm water, under oars, a good pram and a skiff-type flat-bottomed dinghy will yield comparable performance. In fact, some have found that a well-designed flat-bottomed pram will perform nearly as well as a much more expensive round-bottomed dinghy, as long as the pram's bow transom is out of the water. Of course there are round-bottomed prams, too, and the abilities of these little boats will be considered in the following section. Like the flat-bottomed skiff, the flat-bottomed pram is a rare commodity in the production dinghy market. But if you seek the maximum performance and carrying capacity from the smallest-size dinghy, give serious consideration to one of the prams listed in the plans section (Chapter 7). You won't be sorry.

The Immortal Tortoise

In August 1979, *Small Boat Journal* magazine published the plans for a straight-sided punt designed by Phil Bolger. This 6-foot 5-inch boat reflected its creator's typical good sense. Unpretentious in the extreme, Tortoise was intended as a disposable boat that would be unattractive to thieves. Plans were made available by Harold Payson of South Thomaston, Maine, and soon these little punts could be found nosing into dinghy floats in many Maine harbors. With an afterdeck that both stiffens the hull and makes it possible to launch the boat from deck or dock without shipping water, Tortoise can also be fitted with a sailing rig. Plans can be ordered from Payson at the address noted in Chapter 7.

Round-Bottomed Dinghies

As a dinghy's length increases to 8 feet and beyond, a rounded bottom becomes increasingly practical. Eight-foot dinghies can be designed to possess

This handsome, wooden 9-foot Lawley tender slips easily through the water. It has high freeboard for seaworthiness when loaded. Lapstrake construction combines strength with reasonably light weight. Note the use of adequate-length oars, protected by leathers, to ensure optimum performance. This traditional, round-bottomed dinghy was built by the Rockport (Maine) Apprenticeshop.

adequate stability, but as length increases toward 12 feet the hull's underwater shape can be refined and slimmed down somewhat, minimizing resistance to forward motion. That reduced resistance, and its potential for enhancing the boat's performance, is the advantage the round-bottomed yacht tender has over other types.

"Gets up to 15 feet per stroke!" is one of the claims for Johannsen Boat Works' Trinka tender, and it pretty well sums up the virtue of good round-bottomed dinghies. They can be excellent performers. If you routinely must row a long distance to your mooring, or are a long-distance cruiser who may have a long row in from an anchorage, then a round-bottomed dinghy's advantages may become a necessity.

There is a long tradition of round-bottomed dinghies. They were popular as yacht tenders, or "lifeboats" (as dinghies were once routinely called), right up until the postwar era, when cruising boats began increasing in number and decreasing in size. A typical round-bottomed dinghy was 10 or 12 feet long, or longer. Full bodied, yet with fine underwater lines, raised sterns, and good freeboard, these were buoyant, good-rowing, able craft. Their rounded bottoms slip easily through the water with none of the pounding occasionally experienced in any flat-bottomed boat. A well-designed 10- or 12-footer can be surprisingly seaworthy, and that can be a comfort—even a necessity—for some cruisers.

With the advent of fiberglass construction, it became a simple matter to copy or refine the shapes of the old dinghies on a production basis at far less cost than that of a comparable wooden boat. Today, many, if not most, of the larger fiberglass dinghies are the result of molds taken off one of the old wooden boats. These designs are well-proven, and, particularly if rowing and sailing performance is of primary importance to you, such dinghies are worth a close look.

The popular 12-footer produced in Maine by Jarvis Newman reflects the adaptations for fiberglass construction made to a century-old design. Newman's tender is based on a boat once built by Arthur Spurling of Islesford, Maine. Spurling built 25 or 30 of his rowboats, a few of which are still afloat and cherished to this day by those who own them. Newman made slight modifications to yield a more pronounced, wineglass stern, and he rounded off corners as necessary so the hull could be lifted from the mold. The sheer was lowered 1 1/2 inches because the fiberglass version, at 150 pounds, is exactly half the weight of the original and does not sit as deeply in the water. The lowered sheer thus improves the boat's looks and helps position the oarlocks at a proper height.

Other changes involved lowering the boat's transom to match the new sheerline and to make an outboard more practical. Foam flotation was added, as well as a rather wide, sturdy keel, rare in a fiberglass dinghy of any model. Its robust proportions not only help the boat track in a straight line but also absorb the punishment of rocky bottoms and beaches. (The need for such keels or bottom strakes is discussed in Chapter 3.)

Although dinghies such as Newman's are rare, there are other tenders on the market derived from handsome, able tenders of the past. The Whitehall boat

Jarvis Newman and his tender. This 12-foot, round-bottomed boat was adapted from a century-old rowboat. Fine-lined by comparison with smaller tenders, it rows and tows with ease.

A traditional lapstrake dinghy. This 7-foot 9-inch lapstrake tender was built by designer Bill Peterson of Bristol, Maine. Its beautifully curved ribs, lapped planks, two sets of oarlocks, roped gunwale, and sculling notch are only some of the features that make such boats so desirable, and expensive.

once so commonly seen as a fast, working small craft has been adapted several times for fiberglass construction as a yacht tender. The original Whitehalls were generally 16 to 18 feet long, with narrow 3- to 4-foot beams. However, some models, intended for use as dinghies, were beamier, and the 12-foot dinghy built by B & S Corporation in Albion, Maine (see Chapter 7) is based on just such a vessel.

There is no practical or desirable way to reduce the length of a 16-foot Whitehall to 10 feet without proportionally increasing its traditionally narrow beam, flattening the curves of the bottom, and adding some fullness aft. Otherwise, the resulting craft would be too tippy and sink too low in the water as gear or passengers are added. Still, some of the derivations available are surprisingly evocative of the originals, and, keeping their limitations in mind, they can make pleasant dinghies. "Even the 12-foot and 13-foot Whitehalls did pull very easily," noted Mystic Seaport's John Gardner in *Building Classic Small Craft,* "far easier than most of the scurvy tubs that pass for rowboats today."

What makes a "scurvy tub"? A boat designed for outboard power, with broad, flat surfaces aft to support the motor and help the boat plane, is a far cry from the hull shape that can be rowed easily. In a typical aluminum skiff, you can sometimes *hear* the water dragging along the boat's bottom as you pull on what are invariably a set of too-short oars. Such boats aren't scurvy tubs when used with outboard power, but they hardly qualify as *"rowboats"*. They are designed to operate not at rowing speed, but at the much higher speeds to which an outboard can drive the boat. In contrast to the flat aftersections of such a boat, the well-designed round-bottomed dinghy will have an entirely different bottom configuration, with an effort made to let the water close behind the boat as easily as it does when the bow parts it.

The V-Bottomed Dinghy

If the flat-bottomed dinghy offers the ultimate in initial stability, and the round-bottomed dinghy offers the ultimate in performance, the V-bottomed boat falls somewhere in between. These hard-chine dinghies typically have bottoms with shallow deadrise, flat surfaces for much of their length aft, and gracefully hollowed-out bow sections. If well designed, such a hull must push aside somewhat less water than a flat-bottomed boat, and thus can—all else being equal—be easier to row a long distance. The V-shaped bottom helps the boat track in a straight line and adds some lateral resistance under water that a flat-bottomed boat inherently lacks. Back aft, the wide bottom delivers good performance under power, and most such boats offer acceptable stability.

Perhaps the first and most famous such dinghy was designed during World War II by Philip Rhodes and Charles Wittholz in response to a Navy request for a dinghy that would fit in the 9-foot space available aboard a PT boat. That plywood dinghy was to become famous after the war as the Dyer Dhow. By 1952, molds had been made to produce the boat in the then-new medium of

This hard-chine, V-bottomed Dyer dinghy was developed for plywood construction and use aboard PT boats in World War II. Well balanced in reasonably smooth water, it gives its crew a dry ride.

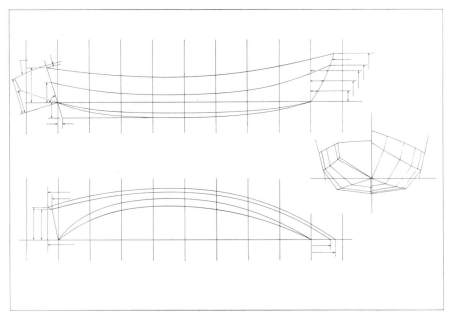

A V-bottomed dinghy for homebuilders. Newport, Rhode Island, designer Eric Sponberg developed the 9-foot Chula *to offer better performance than most flat-bottomed boats.*

fiberglass. Soon, the general design was being copied widely, and today, boats of this general type are among the most commonly seen dinghies, available in a wide range of prices from a number of different builders.

Hard-chine, V-bottomed dinghies lend themselves well to amateur construction out of plywood, and there are a number of plans and kits available for such boats. They lack the compound curves possible with fiberglass construction, but some, such as the B & B Yacht Designs prams or the Nutshell pram kit sold by *WoodenBoat,* are extremely good-looking boats.

Dories and Peapods

Inevitably, the idea of using a traditional-style boat for a yacht tender arises from time to time, and, occasionally, one sees a dory or peapod being towed behind a traditional-style cruising boat. Although the wisdom of this approach is questionable for most boatowners, a certain tradition does exist for using such craft as dinghies.

In April 1895, when he set off on his solo voyage around the world, Joshua Slocum carried a dinghy stowed on the *Spray's* deck. It was a Cape Ann dory that he had cut in half, "boarding up the end where it was cut. . . . Manifestly, there was not room on deck for more than half of a boat which, after all, was better than no boat at all, and was large enough for one man. I perceived, moreover, that the newly arranged craft would answer for a washing machine when placed athwartships, and also for a bath-tub." Slocum was nearly drowned seven months into his voyage when this 9-foot-long boat capsized in surf while he tried to carry out an anchor from the grounded *Spray.*

L. Francis Herreshoff considered the Cape Ann dory "the worst possible yacht tender. It tows poorly, rows poorly in a breeze, and is most difficult to get in and out of. This model is utterly useless when reduced in sizes below 16 feet O.A."

The desire to use such craft as yacht tenders appears to be based on myth and romance, rather than reality. Anyone who has read anything about nineteenth-century dory fishermen comes away with an immense respect for the men as well as the boats, which were praised uniformly for their seaworthiness. These fishing dories were essentially double-ended, flat-bottomed, hard-chine boats with a lot of flare in their topsides planking. They were heavily loaded with gear, and eventually with fish, gaining ever more stability as the load increased. Empty, however, the true dory is a tippy vessel. Its flaring sides give it good ultimate resistance to capsize, but it's not a reliable boat for day-to-day dinghy use.

So-called dory tenders do exist. Their bottoms are proportionally wide compared to that of a fishing dory, increasing their suitability for use as dinghies. Even these boats are generally tender, however, and take some getting-used-to.

Another double-ender occasionally pressed into service as a yacht tender is the peapod. There have been countless variations on the peapod theme, and

The semidory. Flat-bottomed semidories, beamier than a traditional dory and with a transom stern, have much in common with flat-bottomed skiffs and can make suitable tenders.

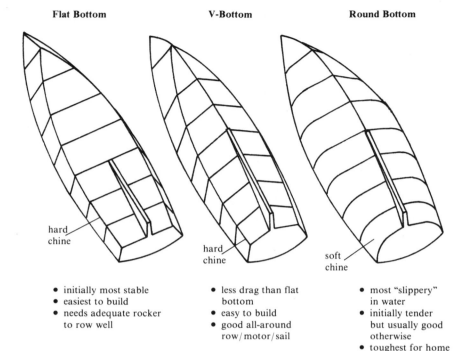

Flat Bottom   **V-Bottom**   **Round Bottom**

hard chine

hard chine

soft chine

- initially most stable
- easiest to build
- needs adequate rocker to row well

- less drag than flat bottom
- easy to build
- good all-around row/motor/sail

- most "slippery" in water
- initially tender but usually good otherwise
- toughest for home builder

these boats served generations of Maine fishermen, who used them to tend nets and traps and towed them behind their Friendship sloops. Most peapods were 14 to 16 feet long, but smaller versions also existed. Mystic Seaport has a 12-footer in its collection that, if lightly built, might make a good tender. There are also some professionally built peapods on the market.

Peapods are generally notable for their excellent rowing qualities, seaworthiness, and stability. With their buoyant hulls, generous beam, and often moderate deadrise, peapods have always had a certain appeal for yachtsmen who don't mind towing a rather large, heavy dinghy. Because most such boats are carvel-planked, they need to be left in the water so that their seams don't dry out and permit leaks.

Summary of Dinghy Designs
FLAT-BOTTOMED DINGHY

ADVANTAGES	DISADVANTAGES
High initial stability; easy to get in and out of.	When the point of ultimate stability is exceeded, a flat-bottomed boat tips suddenly. Swamped, free-flowing water makes such a dinghy very unstable.
Good rowing performance; fairly dry if designed with adequate rocker and flare.	Tendency to pound in a chop.
Reasonably easy to build by comparison to a round-bottomed boat.	

PRAMS (FLAT-, V-, ROUND-BOTTOMED)

ADVANTAGES	DISADVANTAGES
Great capacity for size.	Looks may be unappealing to some.
Flat-bottomed types are easiest of all for amateur to build.	
Wide variety of plans available.	The number of fiberglass models is limited.
Good prams row very nicely, especially when lightly loaded.	Performance suffers when heavily loaded, as bow may offer increased resistance.

ROUND-BOTTOMED DINGHY

ADVANTAGES	DISADVANTAGES
Smooth lines give best rowing/sailing performance.	Tend to be "tippy" when boarding and leaving, making them most practical in larger (8 feet and over) sizes. Performance with outboard may be only moderate.
Ten-foot to 12-foot length offers good carrying capacity and comfort.	May be longer than most wish to tow (although their smooth lines may offer no more resistance than a poorly designed smaller boat); comparatively heavy (120 to 160 pounds).
Handsome appearance.	Some larger models tend to be expensive.

V-BOTTOMED DINGHY

ADVANTAGES	DISADVANTAGES
Widely available in a broad price range.	Less expensive models may lack durability to withstand sustained hard use.
Reasonably good rowing/sailing performance.	
Performance with outboard is typically excellent.	

DORIES AND PEAPODS

ADVANTAGES	DISADVANTAGES
Dories and peapods offer traditional good looks.	Boats are large, heavy and may, or may not, offer acceptable towing performance.
Dories offer good ultimate stability and seaworthiness if over 12 feet long (bottom length).	Unless heavily loaded, dories are tender ("tippy") and require a lot of getting-used-to when used as yacht tenders.
Semidories offer handsome looks and more stability than traditional fishing dories.	Can be expensive if professionally built, demanding for the amateur builder.
Larger dories have potential as serious lifeboats.	Too large for most sailboats to stow aboard.
Peapods may offer excellent rowing and towing qualities.	Comparatively large if they are to offer adequate stability, wooden peapods are typically carvel-built and must be left in the water to "soak up."

Design Recommendations

- In terms of overall rowing and sailing performance, and load-carrying ability, remember that bigger is almost always better. Consider the largest dinghy you can afford, tow, store, or lug, and remember that the finer lines of the larger boats often mean that towing resistance may be no more, or may even be less, than in some smaller boats.

- Remember that, while fine underwater lines and a comparatively narrow beam create the least resistance when rowing, pulling boats designed primarily for high rowing performance will not possess the stability or load-carrying performance of a boat designed to be a good rowing yacht tender.

- Although a boat's beam may become proportionally narrower as hull length increases, it is unlikely that any dinghy with a beam less than 4 feet will provide adequate stability when entering and leaving the boat and carrying heavy loads.

- If an outboard motor will be your primary source of motive power, select a boat with a broad, flat bottom aft to bear the weight of motor, crew, and gear.

- If you are planning to acquire a dinghy less than 8 feet in length, whether it must be stowed aboard or not, give serious consideration to a flat-bottomed pram or skiff with a properly rockered bottom. But beware of any such boat that appears comparatively narrow in the beam or at the bow, for it is likely to lack stability.

- Use of a traditional workboat, such as a dory, as a yacht tender should be attempted only after full consideration of the trade-offs involved.

CHAPTER THREE

Construction

*D*INGHIES lead difficult lives. They get rolled over, stepped on, slammed against docks, dragged over rocks and sand, dropped, swamped, and otherwise abused. If you want to see the result of all this, take a few minutes to inspect a group of dinghies on any storage rack or float. When you do, you'll see what the boat you're going to buy will be up against in terms of survival. You'll see boats with patched bottoms and repaired thwarts, boats with hastily reinforced oarlock sockets, reinforced bow eyes, and split or broken gunwales.

This chapter discusses why so many dinghies wind up looking as they do, and, indirectly, it discusses prices. All too often, a boat's price is considered by many to the exclusion of questions about its construction. Yet it is a dinghy's basic hull construction, and the attachment of everything from the thwarts to the bow eye and oarlocks, that will determine how satisfactory the boat will be, and for how long. There can be significant price differences in boats that, from a few feet away, look identical. Yet the price reflects directly the amount and type of materials of which the boat is built, the quantity and the quality of its woodwork and hardware. Fortunately, many of these details are easy to evaluate just by inspecting the boat.

The Fiberglass Dinghy

The overwhelming majority of dinghies today are made of fiberglass, laid up either by hand or with the aid of a chopper gun that sprays strands of glass into a mold. Hand lay-up is generally, but not always, typical of more expensive boats, whether they are built on a production basis or in ones and twos by backyard builders.

In hand lay-up, layers of fiberglass cloth and matt are laminated together with resin, and the materials are laid into the mold by the builders using squeegees, rollers, or other tools designed for the purpose. The beauty of the

Molds for a variety of dinghies.

system is that the amount of material is specified precisely and the thickness will be uniform.

As long as the builder ensures that the proper amount of resin is used and that the resin is evenly applied and thoroughly saturates the fiberglass itself, a satisfactory piece will result. Too much resin can create brittleness. Too little resin can result in porous areas through which water can "wick" into the boat along a strand of glass. These "resin-poor" areas are unlikely ever to be spotted by inspection of a completed boat and can be repaired only after discovery. Such problems, however, along with delamination of the glass layers, are rare.

Fiberglass construction that relies on a chopper gun has been a topical subject and hotly debated for years. As a tool designed to speed production, the chopper gun is used by many different types of companies manufacturing parts out of fiberglass—from heavy truck-makers building fiberglass hoods for their big rigs to small-boat builders. In the hands of a skillful, conscientious operator, the chopper gun can lay down a nice, even layer of material. Carelessly applied, however, chopped fiberglass matt will vary in thickness, and the strength and thickness of the part being molded will not be uniform.

Generally, chopper guns are viewed with suspicion and criticized by those who don't use them. Most critics admit that good boats can be built with one, but that the quality depends entirely on the operator's skill. The comment is valid, and those who use the machines are seldom backward about saying so. Most claim they can equal the quality of a hand-laid-up boat at a lower cost. In fact, many dinghy builders typically use a combination of both chopper gun and hand-layup to produce the best possible boats at prices lower than completely hand-laid-up models.

Should you eliminate a boat from consideration because a chopper gun is used in its construction? The answer is a resounding "no!" But do not hesitate to ask the manufacturer or builder just how much, and what sort of, material is in his product. If it has been built using well-applied chopped matt against the gelcoat, followed by layers of hand-laid fiberglass cloth (which permits a smoother finish than either woven roving or matt) and another layer of chopped strands, the boat—at least the hull—should be satisfactory.

What About Hull Liners?

Although the great majority of production dinghies have one-piece hulls, some boats are constructed with an interior hull liner. Unlike solid-hull dinghies with painted or gelcoated interiors that may look unfinished, the smooth, gelcoated liners offer an interior that can be as attractive as the hull itself. The liner also permits foam flotation to be installed out of sight while keeping it well protected from the elements. Areas not filled with foam become air pockets, substantially increasing the boat's flotation. Some may be capable of being rowed even when swamped.

The downside of a liner is that it represents an additional part to the boat. It can complicate the mounting of thwarts and fittings, or hull repair. Dinghies built this way may be—although they are not always—heavier than solid hull types. Speaking generally, it's unlikely there will be less than a 10-pound penalty for a linered versus an unlinered boat—and 10 pounds is a lot when you are moving a boat around on land, especially if it is already pushing the outer limits of weight.

If water does manage to find its way between the liner and the hull, whether through an unseen crack, gap, or hole, it can further increase the boat's weight. The liner can complicate repairs, too. If there is air space between the liner and the hull, or if the space is filled with foam, water can enter and become trapped. That may require drilled holes to let water drain out, and perhaps a drying-out of the foam interior with a hair dryer. Difficulties in drying out the boat will be increased if the builder has used open- rather than closed-cell foam. The former can permit the extensive migration of water into the hull. Thus, it is worth asking *what sort of foam* has been used in any dinghy built with a liner.

Many boats without full liners have, in effect, partial liners at the bow and stern, in the form of flotation chambers. These must be well-glassed-in all around; otherwise, they may leak. Leak-testing is even more important on boats with air tanks forward and aft than it is on boats with foam-filled chambers. Dinghies with such flotation tanks, which allow storage access through removable hatches, should be pressure-tested by their builder to ensure integrity. Although most builders who install air-tank flotation forward or aft specify that they pressure-test their boats, be sure to ask if they have done so. Remember, too, to take care when it comes to maintaining such dinghies, and carefully patch any possible leaks.

"Lapstrake" Fiberglass Dinghies

Although most fiberglass dinghies are smooth-sided, a number of boats are available that mimic the lapped planks of a wooden boat. Such construction can offer several advantages. First, the presence of the "laps" increases the boat's stability somewhat—all those little surfaces do add up, creating resistance that makes the boat somewhat less tippy. Second, the horizontal ridges and angles created by the molded "planks" add longitudinal stiffness to the hull, while still retaining some athwartships flexibility. That means there's some give in case you crunch the dinghy between your boat and a dock.

The increased stiffness of molded lapstrakes makes it possible for such a dinghy to be built somewhat lighter than a smooth-sided boat, which must rely entirely on hull thickness for strength. Not all builders take advantage of the opportunity this type of construction offers for weight savings, or they sometimes lose the weight advantage to liners or other parts. A check of the dinghies listed in Chapter 7 will give you an indication of the comparative weights of lapstrake and smooth-sided models.

Gunwales and Rubrails

Among the most obvious clues to a boat's quality, price, and long-term durability is the construction of the gunwale and rubrail. The most common

Hard use and light construction. The flanged gunwale and rubrail of this dinghy are clearly in trouble. The thwart has required beefing-up, too.

This Cape Cod Shipbuilding MK Dinghy has a unique gunwale, and a separate "deck" molding that runs around the hull and reinforces this key area.

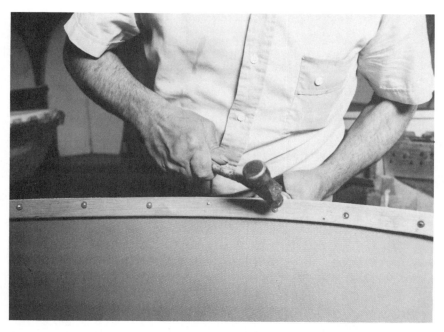

Premium quality at the gunwale. Oak inner and outer wales riveted together provide perhaps the very best, and most costly, method of forming this important part. Here, a Dyer dinghy is nearing completion.

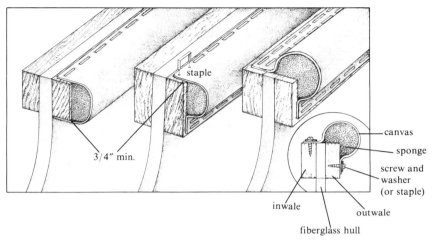

To further protect your dinghy (and others) from the crush at the dinghy dock, as well as to protect your yacht's topsides, consider installing industrial-strength gunwale guards made of canvas-covered sponge rubber. These are readily available at most chandleries for about $3.25 per running foot, and are easily installed.

Half-round guards can be installed with stainless steel or bronze screws. To prevent damage to overhanging topsides they can be fastened with stainless or monel staples or laced in place with stainless or monel seizing wire passed through holes drilled vertically through the gunwale.

For ultimate protection of overhanging topsides, choose three-quarter round guards. These can be fastened with closely spaced screws. Insufficiently fastened three-quarter round guards are easily "rolled off" the gunwale by hard rubbing.

gunwale is a fiberglass flange extending outward from the sheer, usually covered by a rubber or plastic rubrail attached by pop rivets, nylon screws, or glue. These flanged gunwales are fairly strong, and may serve for years, particularly if the boat is *not* rolled over before and after each use. It is the rolling action that eventually breaks such gunwales and rubrails—a consideration because the great majority of dinghies are stored upside down on racks or floats. The eventual breakdown of such flanges and the separation of the rubrails is almost certain if the boat is rolled over with any frequency.

The alternative to a flanged gunwale is significantly more expensive. The sheer is sandwiched with inner and outer wales, usually oak or mahogany attached with screws, although copper rivets are preferable. Soft, canvas-covered rubber rubrails attached with Monel or stainless steel staples and stainless steel wood screws add further protection. The resulting gunwale, which completely eliminates the flange, can withstand a lot of punishment.

Thwarts

Thwarts, or seats, are worth your close attention, both in terms of their location and the method by which they are attached to the hull. If mislocated, thwarts can significantly detract from your rowing performance; if the bow or stern seat is too high (either to better support the mast or enclose adequate flotation), it can detract from the boat's stability. If the rowing thwart is mounted too high, it can affect not only stability but rowing, because the oars will enter the water at an awkward angle. A bow seat that is too low, too high, or too small can even be found on some otherwise-outstanding dinghies—which is a shame.

Today, thwarts are most commonly supported in fixed positions by risers mounted on the hull, or set atop boxlike structures filled with foam flotation. Ideally, a 1/2-inch gap should be left between the ends of the thwart and the hull. This reduces the chances of accidentally driving the thwart right through the hull, should the dinghy be caught between your hull and a piling. View with suspicion the wooden thwart firmly butted against the sides of the hull.

A number of boats have thwarts that are supported by longitudinal flotation tanks running the length of the hull and forming what is essentially an island up the center. By sacrificing interior volume, such boats gain some worthwhile advantages, among them torsional rigidity. That is, their hulls

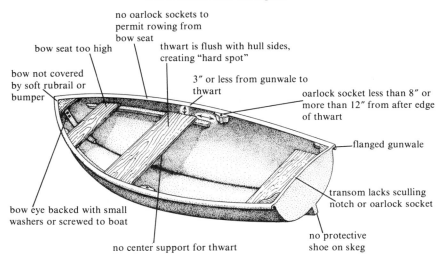

Some Weak Points of Dinghies

no oarlock sockets to
permit rowing from
bow seat

bow seat too high

thwart is flush with hull sides,
creating "hard spot"

bow not covered
by soft rubrail or
bumper

3″ or less from gunwale to
thwart

oarlock socket less than 8″ or
more than 12″ from after edge
of thwart

flanged gunwale

transom lacks sculling
notch or oarlock socket

bow eye backed with small
washers or screwed to boat

no center support for thwart

no protective
shoe on skeg

tend to be structurally stiff and highly resistant to twisting. In addition, the uniform width between the flotation tanks permits the use of identically sized thwarts that are interchangeable, should one be broken, and often are adjustable fore and aft, permitting easy trimming of the boat, whatever its load. Finally, flotation encapsulated longitudinally along the hull ensures that the dinghy will remain level if swamped, because the flotation material is so evenly distributed.

The thwarts, and their *relation* to the gunwale and oarlock positions, are central to a boat's performance. They will make the oarsman comfortable or uncomfortable, and thus directly affect his efficiency. Most builders have found that 6 or 7 inches is an ideal thwart width. The rower slides around less on a narrow seat; a wider thwart takes up valuable space, and, particularly in a very small boat, represents just one more obstruction for entry or exit.

Thwarts are often varnished to a high gloss, which may enhance sales appeal, but there's more to be said for giving them a good, nonskid finish or making them of unfinished teak. Either can help keep you from sliding around. The intention is *not* to provide a nonslip finish on which *to step!*

A Proper Rowing Pram

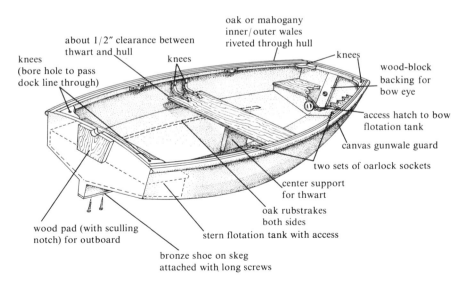

knees
(bore hole to pass
dock line through)

about 1/2″ clearance between
thwart and hull

knees

oak or mahogany
inner/outer wales
riveted through hull

knees

wood-block
backing for
bow eye

access hatch to bow
flotation tank

canvas gunwale guard

two sets of oarlock sockets

center support
for thwart

oak rubstrakes
both sides

stern flotation tank with access

wood pad (with sculling
notch) for outboard

bronze shoe on skeg
attached with long screws

The interrelationship between thwart and oarlocks is a tricky business, involving not merely the height of the gunwales and the boat's freeboard, but the depth of the boat—the distance from the gunwale to the lowest point in the hull. If things are really far off—and a few inches is enough here—you may find yourself contorting to keep your hands from hitting your knees when rowing. That may be acceptable when you're rowing by yourself for a short distance, but it quickly becomes tiring when the boat is heavily loaded and you have a long distance to cover.

Fairly consistent dimensions have been established for the positioning of oarlocks in relation to thwarts, with suggestions ranging from 8 1/2 to 12 inches aft of the thwart's after edge (the range advocated by the American National Red Cross standard), depending on the designer. The height of the thwart, from the bottom of the boat and from the top of the gunwale, is another question. A lifetime of experience suggested to boat designer and builder R.D. ("Pete") Culler that thwarts positioned 10 inches from the bottom and 7 inches from the rail were just about perfect.

Straying much from these dimensions generally results in an inefficient and uncomfortable rowing position for most people. Culler's dimensions suggest a boat with a minimum *depth* (distance from top of gunwale to bottom of hull) of 17 inches. Depth is not always mentioned in spec sheets, but it clearly is

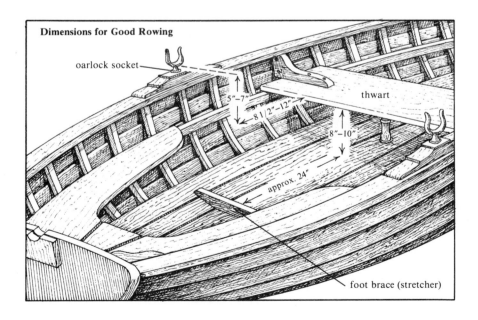

Dimensions for Good Rowing

oarlock socket

5"–7"

8 1/2"–12"

thwart

8"–10"

approx. 24"

foot brace (stretcher)

important—both to thwart and oarlock location and to freeboard. *Too little* depth makes it almost impossible to achieve an effective rowing position or adequate carrying capacity and seaworthiness.

Note that you *cannot* take for granted that a dinghy's oarlock sockets will be properly located. One fairly pricey dinghy, now out of production, actually had its thwarts mounted *flush* with the gunwales. Other boats have sockets located from just a few inches to a ridiculous 16 inches from the thwart, and only 2 or 3 inches from the top of the rail! The latter suggests a boat of low freeboard with oars that will scrape your knees. Note, too, that it may sometimes be useful, or even necessary, to row from the bow seat. That requires a second set of *reasonably well-located* oarlock sockets, and a bow seat that is not so high that it impairs stability. Many boats don't have either.

It is worth pointing out that the other aid to really efficient rowing, the stretcher for bracing the feet, is seldom found in any production dinghy. On the very smallest of boats, you may be able to brace your feet against the transom. But, particularly if you are dealing with a small shop making a boat specifically for you, consider adding a stretcher to the boat's bottom, located a bit off the centerline for greatest efficiency. A suggestion for a stretcher is shown on page 118.

An Old-Timer's Thoughts on Thwarts

"Another very particular point in the fitting of yachts' boats is the placing of the thwarts, rowlocks and stretchers, so as to enable the rowers to exercise their muscular powers with the most beneficial effect: if the thwarts are placed too high or too low, the rowlocks too near or too far, and the stretcher not so as to give a good purchase to the feet, the best man that ever handles an oar will be at a very serious disadvantage."
—C. William Cooper, *The Yacht Sailor,* circa 1885

A final note on thwarts: A brace running from the center thwart to the keel is a good idea, as it keeps the thwart from flexing and stressing the hull itself. The daggerboard trunk of a sailing dinghy provides just such support, and boats with a central fore-and-aft thwart do, too. Several more expensive models have a boxlike or tube-type support beneath the thwart, and the only downside to such devices is that the boat cannot be nested, thwart removed, over some deck structure. But the sturdiest thwart remains the one that is supported in its middle as well as at its edges.

The importance of a forward rowing position. A second set of oarlock sockets, which many dinghies lack, makes possible proper balance, as seen here in an aluminum dinghy once manufactured by Grumman, a Lowell pram, and an Ensign Sweet Sue.

Protecting the Bottom

Because it is unlikely that you will always have a smooth sand bottom to drag your boat across when you beach it, some sort of protection is desirable for both the bottom and the skeg. Of the two, protection for the skeg—preferably in the form of a metal rub strip—should be considered almost mandatory, but skids on the hull are important, too. They can absorb the punishment of shells and rocks and help protect the hull from abrasion, which may eventually wear right through the gelcoat into the lay-up, allowing water to penetrate. That can happen all too quickly if a boat is very lightly built.

Adding such strakes and skeg protection, however, is labor-intensive, and relatively few builders bother. Those who do either mold in the strakes or attach wooden ones during the building process. Attaching rubbing strakes so

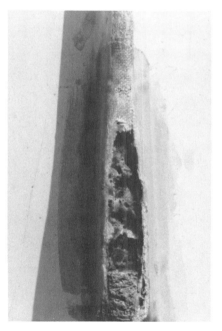 

Skeg with barnacles. Although it's been repaired, this skeg has now been severely damaged by abrasion. A protective shoe would have prevented the problem. A thorough cleaning-out, drying, and filling with hard putty is needed.

An abraded bottom. This dinghy's bottom has been patched. Protective bottom strakes can help avoid the necessity for such repairs.

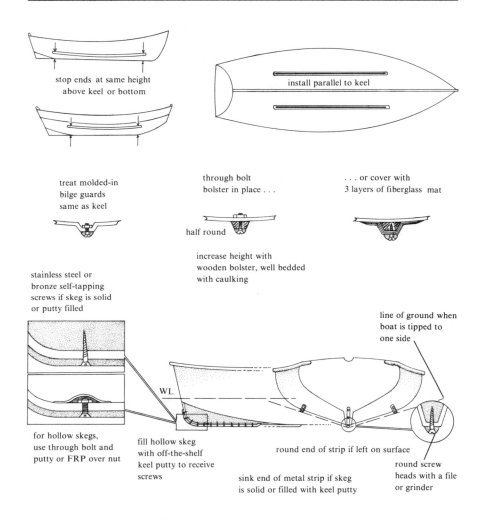

stop ends at same height
above keel or bottom

install parallel to keel

treat molded-in
bilge guards
same as keel

through bolt
bolster in place . . .

half round

. . . or cover with
3 layers of fiberglass mat

increase height with
wooden bolster, well bedded
with caulking

stainless steel or
bronze self-tapping
screws if skeg is solid
or putty filled

line of ground when
boat is tipped to
one side

WL

for hollow skegs,
use through bolt and
putty or FRP over nut

fill hollow skeg
with off-the-shelf
keel putty to receive
screws

round end of strip if left on surface

sink end of metal strip if skeg
is solid or filled with keel putty

round screw
heads with a file
or grinder

If you expect to beach your dinghy frequently, consider adding additional protection to your skeg and bilges. A stainless steel or bronze rubbing strip can be attached to a solid skeg by using self-tapping screws of the same metal as the strip. A hollow skeg should be filled first with an off-the-shelf keel putty to hold the fastenings. Alternatively, use through-bolts with nuts set in body putty, fiberglass, or both.

Wooden bilge bolsters should lie parallel to the keel, just below the turn of the bilge. Fasten them in place with well-bedded through-bolts, or use three layers of fiberglass mat to bond them in place.

that they are not easily broken, and so that bolt or screw holes don't leak is a significant enough problem that some builders who once added strakes have stopped doing so.

The alternative is molded-in strakes, but they are at best a compromise. They do offer a kind of first line of protection, but eventually they suffer the same sort of damage and require the same sort of repair as would the hull. Some builders have had success by using epoxy to attach spruce strips to the turn of the bilge. When the strips wear out, they can be renewed. (Note that protecting the bottom of a flat-bottomed boat is generally somewhat easier than protecting that of a round-bottomed dinghy.) A wooden keel bolted through the hull, to which a removable shoe can be screwed, is a good alternative for those who regularly drag their dinghy up and down rocky beaches.

Wooden skegs can suffer much the same problems as wooden bilge stringers or keels attached by screws or bolts. If they are attached from the inside, as most are, be sure to keep the screws tight. More than one builder has found himself repairing dinghies in which the screws attaching the skeg had been pulled right out through the bottom of the hull.

If you will be dragging your boat across beaches regularly, it should have the minimum protection (offered as an option by many builders) of a stainless steel or brass shoe screwed into the keel. A metal shoe that goes *from bow to stern* is better yet. Protective strips for the hull are available on several production dinghies.

Floorboards

Available as options on most dinghies, floorboards are almost invariably worth consideration. They will help keep feet and gear clear of water that collects in the boat's bottom, and they will protect the inside of the boat from impact. Depending on the hull's shape, the floorboards can also make an easy attachment point for a foot brace. About the only negative aspect of floorboards is their weight, but if that is not a significant consideration, by all means get floorboards.

Oarlocks

Because oarlocks are subjected to significant stress, the area of the gunwale in which they are installed should have at least some reinforcement. On a number of fiberglass boats, particularly ones with flanged gunwales, the sockets appear to offer considerably less strength than required. In flanged gunwales, a good thickness of glass needs to be built up in the area around the socket to resist the torque loads transmitted by the oars. Those loads can cause eventual breakdown of the gunwale and render an oarlock useless.

Should that happen, by the way, all is not lost. A block of oak, bored out to

An oarlock socket that could be improved. Wood backing would do much to strengthen this key component.

An oarlock socket improved. This oarlock socket has been beefed up with a hardwood block to withstand the torque loads imposed when rowing, and to give added strength to the gunwale for times when the boat is rolled over on the dinghy dock or elsewhere.

accept the oarlock, can be inserted into the gunwale and bolted to the hull, rendering the dinghy serviceable once again. But you'll avoid an eventual repair, probably one that needs to be rushed, by taking protective action and installing the wooden blocks *before* any damage occurs.

Dinghies with wooden gunwales usually have at least adequate oarlock installations. Generally, the oarlocks are set into a generous-sized piece of wood and held firmly in place with large screws. A through-bolted socket with a backing plate to take the load of the bolts and tightened nuts is also a good arrangement.

Dinghies are typically fitted with one of three kinds of oarlocks: galvanized, bronze, or a nylonlike plastic material. Of the three, bronze is generally preferable. Good-quality galvanized fittings have apparently become rare to nonexistent these days, and once the galvanizing wears off the oarlock, rust sets in quickly. The nylon locks, while they may look flimsy, generally perform quite well, resisting wear and breakage.

A good oarlock socket will withstand years of hard use. This one is through-bolted to a piece of oak.

The Bow Eye

The bow eye will typically be located just above the waterline, or somewhat higher on the stem, in a position that generally results in the most docile towing performance. Solid reinforcement of the towing eye is essential—especially so if you need to tow your dinghy in poor weather, when it is likely to take on water, dramatically increasing its weight.

Check to see what reinforcement, if any, the dinghy has in the bow area behind the towing eye. At a minimum, the fiberglass in the stem area should be built up to a good thickness and the eye itself should be bolted through the stem, the bolts secured against a metal backing plate to prevent the bow eye from being ripped out. Sometimes, the bow eye is a bronze or stainless steel ring rather than an eyebolt. Such a ring should be large enough to accept a reasonable-sized thimble and eyesplice, and the pad eye should be through-bolted to a solid backing. Beware of bow eyes attached only by screws.

The strongest bow-eye installations have a solid block of wood glassed into the stem, through which the bow eye is bolted. Ideally, the nut securing the eye should be peened over so that it cannot work loose. Bow-eye installation is especially important when the bow seat encloses foam and the bow-eye mount cannot be inspected. Question the builder closely, and if his answer is not satisfactory, consider looking elsewhere. Note that if you plan to splice your painter to the bow eye (rather than using a *substantial* shackle) *and* keep the dinghy on a pull-line, a second bow eye is likely to be required.

This rugged oak breasthook adds strength to the dinghy's bow and has been hollowed out to give a good handhold for pulling or lifting. A large eye, solidly mounted, serves as the attachment point for the painter.

How to Improve the Basic, Low-Cost Dinghy

Lower-priced dinghies usually get that way because they lack the details that escalate the price of more expensive boats. Several steps can be taken to improve the lower-priced dinghy: (1) Use bolts to attach hardwood mounts for new, bronze oarlock sockets between the flange and the hull. If possible, and if your boat is reasonably beamy toward the bow, add a *second* set of sockets about 10 inches aft of the bow seat. (2) Add an oarlock socket to the transom so you can scull your dinghy. (3) Add a vertical upright support for the center thwart to prevent its flexing. If the hull beneath the thwart is not full thickness because of a hollow skeg, fill in the skeg beneath the upright with an epoxy putty such as Marine-Tex, a polyester casting resin (with or without an inert filler added), or an off-the-shelf keel putty. (4) If the bow eye is in any way questionable in terms of dimensions or mounting, reinforce or replace it with a bow eye that has a wooden backing block. (5) Use bolts to mount bow and stern cleats if there is no other convenient way to make lines fast to your dinghy. (6) Use a piece of quarter-round or half-round bronze, about 3/8 inch wide, to make a shoe for your boat's skeg. Use bedding compound and, if the skeg is solid enough, long screws to attach the skeg. Otherwise, through-bolt the strip.

Wood Construction

The traditional wooden yacht tender of lapstrake construction is almost invariably a beautiful boat that combines reasonably light weight with excellent rowing performance and load-carrying capacity. Because the planks require no caulking, such dinghies don't need to swell up after being ashore, and they are always ready to go. Despite these attributes, such boats are seldom practical for more than the smallest segment of buyers because professionally built examples are so expensive. This is not to suggest the boats aren't worth the money! A wooden boat of any size represents one of the few truly functional, handmade objects one can buy these days. The problem is that most people aren't prepared to pay, or can't afford to pay, the price. Those who are must also be prepared to do a certain amount of maintenance and consider the greater difficulty in making repairs than exists with a fiberglass boat. For all these reasons, the traditionally built wooden dinghy makes the most sense for the well-to-do boatman, or home builder, who will use it primarily in home waters or for the yearly vacation cruise.

Quite different in concept and execution, and far more affordable, is the plywood dinghy, for which many plans, and a few kits, are available. Listings for both appear in Chapter 7. Plywood has a negative connotation to some—a

A strongback like this is the form over which wooden small craft can be built on a semiproduction basis. Here, the keel of a Columbia tender is set in place at Rivendell Marine.

result perhaps of problems experienced with boats not built of *marine* plywood. Cheap plywood is nasty-looking stuff, full of voids (gaps) between its layers. High-quality plywood, however, is a beautiful and costly material that is exceptionally tough, and stronger pound-for-pound than steel. In one test by a company that builds sleeper cabs for big trucks, plywood floorboards were found to offer substantially more resistance to crushing in accident situations than floorboards made of aluminum.

Not only is marine plywood a viable boatbuilding material in its own right, but, when used in conjunction with the WEST System—Wood/Epoxy Saturation Technique—it offers maintenance requirements similar to those of fiberglass. At the expense of somewhat increased weight and cost, epoxy forms a durable, water-resistant coating that can prolong the already-long lifespan of good plywood indefinitely. Those intrigued with a plywood design and not wanting to build the boat themselves might find they can afford to have one professionally built at a cost comparable to that of a fiberglass model.

Traditional Boats and the WEST System at Lowell's Boat Shop

Among the few wooden dinghies turned out on a production basis are the skiffs available from the oldest boatshop in America, Lowell's Boat Shop in Amesbury, Massachusetts. Epoxy coatings were introduced here in 1976, and, according to the shop's proprietor, Jim Odell, the move has been entirely successful. "We can do more with the dry strength of wood," he says. "We don't have to worry about how strong the wood will be after it starts to soften up from absorbing moisture."

The epoxy permits the use of pine rather than less obtainable and more expensive cedar. Epoxy-coated pine or cedar is generally used for planking, oak for the tender's frames, mahogany for transoms. Usually, the bottoms are fiberglassed—gaining durability and, unfortunately, weight.

The alternative to traditionally constructed wooden dinghies or plywood boats are those built by the process known as "cold-molding." Composed of epoxy-saturated layers of cedar, usually covered with a layer of lightweight fiberglass cloth, the cold-molded boat is typically light, handsome, and sturdy. Routine maintenance involves only an occasional touch-up of paint or varnish. Deep gouges, which might permit water to penetrate the layers of wood, require immediate attention, for water entering the hull will lead to rot.

Because their construction is so labor intensive, the boats are also expensive. Building cold-molded dinghies using the vacuum-bag method—thus avoiding the time-consuming stapling together of each of the many strips of wood composing a cold-molded boat—has thus far not been applied on a production basis.

With wooden dinghies, as with larger wooden boats, a builder's experience is vital. Only after completing a number of boats and observing how they fare under everyday use does a builder develop an instinct for and knowledge of what works, for everything from bending a plank to fashioning small details. Gunwale guards, for instance, are just as important on wooden tenders as on fiberglass models. If the guard is fashioned of rope, it is likely to have leather end caps, and these are best affixed with small screws, rather than brads or escutcheon pins, so the gunwale guard can be renewed. Wooden dinghies that will be outboard-powered need strong transoms with adequate knees and cleats, and a thwart that will absorb the motor's weight, thrust, and vibration without loosening fasteners. Lacking this attention to detail, a dinghy is likely to require an undue amount of maintenance and repairs.

What About Building It Yourself?

A wide variety of intriguing dinghy plans are available to the home builder and, for anyone with the space to do so, building one's own tender is worth serious consideration. Not only is there the satisfaction gained from building your own boat, but many of the available designs have great merit. Several of the prams, in particular, offer exceptional performance, looks, light weight, and, if built of good marine plywood, durability. Many boats requiring no lofting of molds for the frames may be built of sheet plywood. Several kit boats are available, too. (See Chapter 7.)

Construction Summary and Recommendations

- Fiberglass is the material of choice for the great majority of dinghy buyers, with marine plywood an excellent alternative for the home builder.

- The typical flanged gunwale will yield longer life if the dinghy need not be rolled over regularly for storage. Boats with wooden gunwales, particularly those through-bolted or riveted, are the most desirable.

- Proper placement of the oarlock sockets—about 8 to 12 inches aft of the center thwart and about 7 inches above the thwart—is necessary for comfortable, efficient rowing. *Two* sets of oarlock sockets are needed for optimized balance under a variety of load situations.

- A protective shoe on the skeg should be considered necessary if the boat is regularly dragged across rocky beaches.

- The bow eye and oarlock sockets should be reinforced with wood backing and attached not with screws, but bolts.

CHAPTER FOUR

Rigs, Oars, and Outboards

ALTHOUGH most dinghies are rowed or motored, many boats—easily 50 percent or more, according to some builders—are purchased complete with sailing rigs. The notion of sailing your dinghy through a quiet harbor or picturesque anchorage is a pleasant one, and even if many rigs actually see little use, a sailing dinghy is a great deal of fun, whether used for relaxation, teaching sailing, racing, or basic harbor transportation.

It is probably the rig's cost—and the knowledge that it may be used infrequently—that keeps many people from buying the sailing models. Be warned, however, that if you really do plan to sail your dinghy frequently, you should definitely try it before you buy it. Satisfying performance is difficult to achieve in a very small boat. You may well find that the dinghy that scoots you quickly downwind may be nearly impossible to sail back home, or that the sail area has been so minimized—presumably because of safety considerations or a desire to avoid adding reef points to a larger sail—that performance is dismal in a very light breeze.

Whether a rig comes with the boat or is added later, its design requires careful thought. Unfortunately, builders realize that the most appropriate rigs for tiny sailboats may be unfamiliar to most of today's sailors. Such rigs include the lug, sprit, and, to a lesser extent, gaff. As most builders of small boats have learned, anything that is *different* can be a sales impediment, so nearly all the boats you see will have a marconi rig.

Marconi Rigs

Also known as Bermudian, leg-o'-mutton, and jibheaded, this rig is based on a triangular sail—as opposed to the four-sided gaff, lug, and spritsails it has almost entirely replaced. Going from a four-sided to a three-sided sail, however, requires a taller mast in order to set a sail of comparable area. The stays and shrouds necessary to support that taller mast evoke the rigging of a

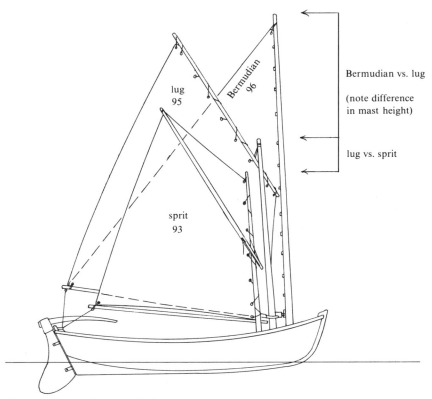

Bermudian vs. lug

(note difference
in mast height)

lug vs. sprit

Marconi, lug, and sprit sailplans. Compared to a triangular sail, the lug or sprit rig offers comparable or greater sail area on a shorter mast, with better overall stability.

radio mast, hence the rig's name. Whatever it's called, the rig will be familiar to everyone. It is simple to operate, with its halyard and mainsheet, and it is reasonably efficient. (Some dinghy builders provide a sleeved sail that must be slipped over the mast, a generally cumbersome task that results in no functional advantage of which I am aware.)

The downside to having a marconi rig for a dinghy is that the mast must be made in two pieces if it is to be stowed within the boat. Any hardware necessary to join the mast sections represents hardware that can be lost. As the boat's size increases, its rig can become unwieldy, 15 feet or more on a 10-footer. That raises the possible need for shrouds, which again represent added parts, and this makes it likely that the mast will need to be unstepped if the boat is not to capsize at a mooring.

A marconi or jibheaded sail, like that of this Ensign Sea Hawk, is typical of today's dinghies. A boomed, rather than a loose-footed sail, eliminates the problem of maintaining an efficient sheeting angle. The mast must be two-piece, if it is to be stored within the boat.

Gunter Rigs

The gunter rig offers the opportunity of retaining a triangular sail—with its long leading edge and the advantage in windward performance it offers—but on a *shorter mast*. The mast height is extended by the yard, which may be hoisted by a halyard or mounted in a fixed position. The latter will never jam and provides a secure way of keeping the yard in line with the mast. The former allows more flexibility in raising and lowering the sail.

The gunter rig's short mast is easier to step than a marconi's longer spar, something to consider as boat size increases. Furthermore, when the sail is reefed, the yard itself is lowered to the same height as the head of the sail, reducing windage when you most want to do so. Unless a sturdy arrangement of jaws and halyard leads has been devised, the yard can sag off to leeward, especially when reefed. But this is less a problem in dinghies—which seldom are fitted with reef points—than it is in larger boats.

The jog in the sail's luff can present a problem if a sailmaker seeks to follow it, rather than making the luff straight, but the difference in efficiency between a gunter sail and a marconi is unlikely to be either noticeable or important for

Gunter rigs, like the one on this Oxford Dinghy, permit a comparatively short mast and yard that can be stowed inside the dinghy.

a yacht tender. The 10-foot 10-inch Mirror dinghy, enormously popular in England, where it was created as a one-design class, is equipped with a gunter sloop rig. Quite a number of decent-performing yacht tenders are also fitted with gunter rigs.

Lug Rig

A few years before he died, sailmaker Colin Ratsey shared with me his opinion that the rig he liked best for a dinghy was a *standing* lug rig. The large sail area possible on a low mast reduces the heeling moment (tendency to tip) of the boat without sacrificing performance; the boat can be tacked without lowering the yard and shifting it from one side of the mast to the other, like a *dipping* lug (which has advantages, too, but not ones that will do a dinghy sailor much good). Several dinghies are available with lug rigs, and they are described in Chapter 7.

Sprit Rig

The sprit rig enjoys many of the same advantages as the lug, but its mast is shorter yet for a comparable sail area, reducing heeling tendencies still further.

The lugsail of this 12-foot North Shore tender permits a large and low sailplan.

The sprit itself, secured to the mast by its snotter tackle, can be adjusted quickly. On breezy days, drive can be taken out of the sail by tensioning the snotter and flattening the sail. On calmer days, the sprit can be pulled forward, adding camber and driving force. Operation of the snotter may be mildly intimidating at first glance, but it performs much the same function as an outhaul.

Spritsails may be used with or without booms or "sprit booms." Either way, reefing can be involved, and a dinghy with a sprit rig large enough to require reefing is a dubious proposition.

Gaff Rig

Occasionally, an 11- or 12-foot dinghy is fitted with a gaff rig. Besides being good looking, such rigs enjoy some of the same advantages as the gunter, sprit, and lug: a comparatively large sail can be set on a mast shorter than that required for a marconi sail. The gaff is lowered together with the sail when reefing is required, and a certain flexibility is gained by the ability to "scandalize" sail—reduce its area by slacking away on the peak halyard. For

Chula's *sprit rig combines a large sail with short, easily handled spars. The sail's draft can be changed for different wind conditions by adjusting the sprit forward or aft.*

Gaff rigs, like the one on this Newman tender, offer excellent performance and are particularly practical on larger dinghies.

dinghies, however, the gaff rig can become complicated, what with the gaff, hardware, two halyards, and a topping lift. (A gaff rig can have a single halyard, but some flexibility is lost in terms of sail shape and control.) Not all the spars of a gaff-rigged dinghy may fit within the hull. That can be a decided disadvantage unless there is space to store them on board, or unless the boat is used primarily as a daysailer.

Spars—Aluminum or Wood?

Most sailing dinghies today are equipped with aluminum spars, which are less expensive than spruce, although less buoyant. One builder who tried identically sized spars of each material found the wooden mast would support a significantly greater amount of weight and still float. Aluminum spars should be foam-filled to enhance flotation. Buyers examining a dinghy's aluminum spars should check the method by which fittings (such as the cast-aluminum jaws of a gunter rig's yard and boom) are attached to the tubing of the spars themselves. Often, they are secured by pop rivets, which can and will corrode, resulting in separation of the parts. Considering that a dinghy's spars not only may be wet frequently, but also may be stored wet, this potential problem is significant. Wood spars require some care and maintenance, but their fittings are easily inspected and, usually, easily repaired.

Booms, Sprit Booms, or No Booms

The simplest dinghy rig would include a boomless sail, thus eliminating a head-thwacking spar and any hardware mounted on it, and also permitting the sail to be stowed readily, wrapped around the mast. Particularly when a lugsail or spritsail is left boomless, there exists the opportunity for a very low sailplan, enhancing stability and possibly ensuring that reef points will not be needed, despite the sail's area.

However, the sheetlead of such a sail (the angle at which the sheet leads from the clew of the sail to the point on the boat where the sheet is attached) presents a significant problem. The position at which the sheet is led properly on one point of sailing usually cannot be maintained on others. If good overall performance is to be achieved, one or two additional sets of sheetleads may be required.

The placement of satisfactory sheetleads depends in part on the boat's shape. Boats that are wide aft offer more satisfactory sheeting angles, and the sail can be sheeted farther from the fore-and-aft centerline. A tubby dinghy can work well with a boomless sail (several such rigs include a simple traveler), although it may not set well off the wind unless an oar is used as a makeshift "spinnaker pole."

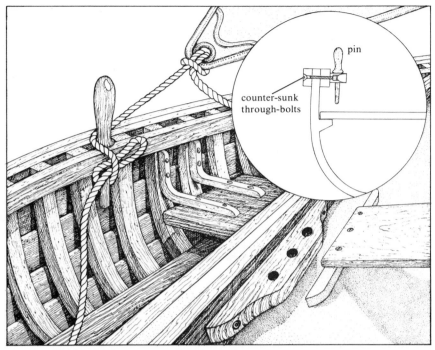

Movable sheet leads, using a wooden pin to which the sheet is attached with a "slippery hitch," are added easily to wooden dinghies with open gunwales. If it breezes up, yank on the bitter end of the sheet, or pull the pin straight up, to let the sheet run free.

Fiberglass dinghies, or wooden ones with solid gunwales, will need to have pinrails added. Clamp them in place and try them out, running and close hauled, before drilling the mounting holes. Make sure they won't interfere with the oarlocks.

The only boomless dinghies I have experienced were small ones that sailed well on one point of sailing only, because the matter of sheetleads had not been solved properly. Still, a couple of dinghies on the market have boomless rigs that work at least as well as many of those with booms.

The addition of a boom solves the problem of sheetleads, and most dinghies have booms with loose-footed sails. In theory, that allows the airfoil shape to be maintained across the sail's foot. But whatever advantage may be gained is probably minimized by the air that spills out between the sail's foot and the boom—one reason why a number of loose-footed sails are cut with some roach to the foot as a compensating, area-increasing measure. It might be noted, too, that a loose-footed sail is less costly than one that requires hardware, or even grommets for a laceline, to attach it to the boom.

Although ultimate efficiency is unlikely to be a requirement in a sailing yacht tender, those who have experimented with both loose-footed sails and a sail attached along its foot to the boom have noted differences. Essex sailmaker Tom Clark found that his boat sailed better with the sail attached to the boom over its full length. "When I sailed her loose-footed," he said, "she was bad in stays. It was a dramatic difference. As soon as I detached the slides along the boom, the leech would harden up and she didn't want to go around at all."

Gloucester yacht designer Phill Bolger, whose experience and experiments with small boats and rigs of all types is vast, suggests, "It's well established that attaching the foot of the sail to the boom improves drive unless the boom is cocked up very sharply toward the outer end. Reason is presumably an end-plate effect."

Whatever its advantage, a boom requires a boom vang if it is not to lift, and twist the sail, when the boat is being sailed off the wind. Although easily rigged, few dinghies are equipped with vangs, performance not being viewed as *that* important. Even fewer models have a sprit boom. Such booms, mounted about one-sixth of the way up the mast rather than attached at the sail's tack, are self-vanging. When the end of the boom begins to lift, it tensions the sail's foot, and the lift is stopped. Such sails are easy to control and gentle to jibe. If the snotter is belayed aft so the dinghy sailor doesn't have to move to the bow and destabilize the boat, a sprit boom offers an easy way to control sail draft. Obviously, a sprit boom cuts into the sail on one tack, but neither that nor chafe is likely to be an impediment on a dinghy or even on the various cruising sharpies and daysailers that use them.

"Traditional" Rigs

I use the word *traditional* here with misgivings. The word is associated by so many with quaint, old-fashioned ways in an era with a passion for high technology. Worse, traditional rigs are often seen on what copywriters and contemporary yacht designers have forever damned as "character boats." These, it is understood, sacrifice performance to old-fashioned looks that, at least, set them apart from today's look-alike designs, whose high topsides and beamy hulls provide most of the comforts of home—at the expense of diminished "character." Nowhere, however, are the advantages offered by such rigs as the lug, gaff, and gunter so worth considering as in dinghies and other small craft. These rigs offer low sailplans and less tipping force than a triangular sail while still maintaining adequate sail area for good performance; the spars can be short and, usually, one piece; and the rigs require an absolute minimum of hardware. In fact, a sprit or lug rig can easily be designed with no hardware at all.

Daggerboard, Centerboard, or Leeboard

The majority of dinghies are equipped with a daggerboard to gain the necessary lateral resistance for sailing. Compared to a centerboard, daggerboards require no hardware and thus are less costly to produce. They also require a smaller slot in the hull's bottom, which marginally improves performance. Unlike a centerboard, of course, they will not pivot out of the way if you hit something with them.

Whether the boat has a daggerboard or a centerboard, the trunk should be capped with a tight-fitting plug. The trunk itself should be sturdy and reinforced along its base to prevent cracks and leaks. When the boat is not being sailed, the daggerboard should be stowed. Some dinghies have provision for securing the daggerboard beneath the center thwart or against a bulkhead. Wherever it is stowed, the board should be fastened to prevent accidental loss.

An alternative occasionally seen is the leeboard, which has many advantages, whether in a dinghy or larger boat. Mounted outside the gunwale, a leeboard requires no turbulence-inducing slot in the boat's keel which adds drag and can reduce performance. Since there is no case required, no space is taken up

A centerboard, like this lever-operated version on an Oxford Dinghy, is seldom found on small boats. Compared to a daggerboard, it takes up more space, is more complicated and expensive to build, but it's more convenient to use.

A single leeboard, like the one on this Spiffy Dink, is enough for a dinghy. It eliminates a slot in the boat's bottom and a trunk within the hull, yet offers excellent performance.

within the boat. That has the obvious advantage of unobstructed volume within the boat and the less-obvious opportunity to build in a removable thwart so that the dinghy can be stowed upside down on deck over another structure. In wooden construction, the absence of a slot in the keel enhances the boat's strength, and the absence of the case removes a potential source of leaks and maintenance headaches. It also simplifies the home builder's task.

That a leeboard can perform as well as a daggerboard, or outperform it, seems to be a continuing source of surprise and amusement. In his classic, *The Ocean Sailing Yacht,* Donald Street noted that to his astonishment, his dinghy—fitted with a homemade leeboard—outsailed an identical boat with its factory daggerboard. "The science of naval architecture," he joked, "was put back 20 *years.*"

In fact, there is much to be said for leeboards in terms of performance. (We have already noted the absence of a slot through the boat's bottom.) A leeboard also can act to enhance performance, because, as the boat heels, the board digs deeper—just the opposite action of a board mounted on the boat's centerline. Because the designer need not worry about the *size* of the slot in the boat's bottom, the leeboard can be large enough to be truly effective. Although I have no hard data to support it, I would guess that a properly proportioned leeboard would provide equal or greater windward performance at a lower angle of heel than a daggerboard—a comfort in any very small craft.

Mounting a leeboard *can* be fussy, depending on what sort of hardware, if any, is involved. Production dinghies with a leeboard usually have had this problem solved, however, which leaves only the necessity of shifting the board from one side to the other when tacking. This probably isn't necessary for short tacks; depending on the design, there may be only a slight drop in performance with the board carried on the windward side. (The installation is usually small and doesn't protrude enough to present a significant obstacle when coming alongside a larger boat or tying off at a dinghy dock.) Only *you* can decide whether the trade-offs are worth it, but don't reject a leeboard-equipped dinghy just because of the leeboard.

Rudders

There is not a great deal to be said about a sailing dinghy's rudder. It should have enough area to be effective—but, strangely enough, not all rudders do. Only sailing the boat will reveal whether the rudder's size is adequate. One theory suggests that the underwater portions of the rudder and board should be about 13 percent of the sail area.

Not all sailing dinghies are equipped with kick-up rudders. That can lead to problems should the rudder hit the bottom, for it will at the very least stop the boat, and perhaps cause some exciting moments. Opt for a kick-up rudder every time, and make sure rudder hardware is attached sturdily.

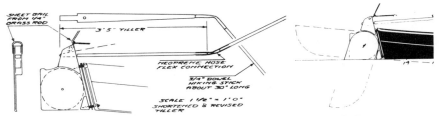

A good example of a kick-up rudder. This one is on Phil Bolger's Gypsy.

Mainly Oars

One of the weaknesses of many little rowing boats is that they don't carry their way to any great degree, tending to slow or even stop between strokes. Good design, as has been shown, can vastly improve the situation. So can a good pair of oars. Few of these are available today, and perhaps relatively few people would appreciate them if they were. Most dinghy builders, recognizing the situation for what it is, choose inexpensive oars to keep their boats' list prices down. There are some, too, who simply feel that expensive oars for a dinghy, as opposed to a nice Whitehall or Rangeley rowboat, are an extravagance. Considering the abuse that a dinghy's oars usually endure—pushing off docks, walls, or the bottom, and being sat, stepped on, and perhaps even stolen—one must be inclined to agree.

But a first-class oar is a satisfying object, and there is no reason why good quality and thoughtful design should not go into oars intended for a dinghy. These days, it is typically the wooden dinghy that will be thoughtfully equipped with oars—thanks mostly to the custom nature of such boats and the attention to details paid by both builder and buyer. The ideal qualities for a

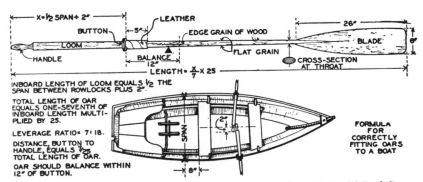

An oar-dimension formula recommended by the American National Red Cross. Much disappointment with rowing can be traced to oars that are too short.

dinghy oar might be summed up as: *appropriate length,* well-balanced, good surface area of the blades, and a design that includes a ridge from the oar's loom to the blade to *cut* the water.

While blade shape becomes crucial in longer oars for longer boats, blade area is more important in a short oar for short boats. "Square inches," points out Maine oarmaker Shaw & Tenney, "is more important in a dinghy than a blade's thickness or its shape. Ideally, you'd talk about a narrow, thin blade, but that's not what you want in a short oar for the smallest boats."

Oar Length

For dinghies, standard oar-length formulas seldom seem to work. Based primarily on beam measurement, they don't take freeboard into account, and sometimes suggest oars too long. Most dinghies have about a 4-foot beam, which would normally indicate a 7 1/2-foot oar. But 6 feet or 6 1/2 feet is likely to stow more handily in boats 8 feet long or less, with 7-footers possible for those who are most serious about rowing.

Even very experienced small-craft designers find that trial-and-error is the best way to select appropriate oars that will just clear each other at the boat's centerline, or else overlap very slightly. For most people, a somewhat-too-short oar initially will seem easier to handle than one that is too long. Such oars will permit a fairly powerful stroke at a comfortable angle. But eventually the rower will recognize the added power possible with a longer oar. Even going from a 6-foot oar to a 6 1/2-foot one can make a significant difference. An 11- or 12-foot dinghy with adequate freeboard might well be fitted with 8-foot oars, a 9-footer with *no shorter than* 6 1/2-foot oars, or, quite possibly, 7-foot oars. Too-short oars will forever condemn you to awkward rowing with

This dinghy is being rowed with oars about a foot too short, which forces the oarsman's hands too high and out to his side, thus reducing power.

This Herreshoff pram, built in Camden, Maine, by Bill Cannell, has appropriate-length oars protected by leathers.

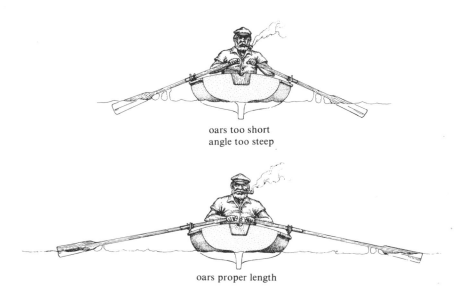

oars too short
angle too steep

oars proper length

your hands raised too high and the oars entering the water at too steep an angle.

Owners of dinghies 9 feet or longer—or those with smaller boats who plan to do more extensive rowing than from dock to mooring—may want to consider spoon-bladed oars. The smallest spoons made by Shaw & Tenney are

6 1/2 feet. While the price is high enough to approach the point of diminishing returns in terms of performance gained, those who choose spoons usually are glad they did so.

The comparatively short length of most dinghy oars, and the abuse to which they are subjected, means that ash generally is more practical than spruce, which is lighter but not so tough. An ash blade has the advantage that it need not be protected by a metal tip, since the end grain doesn't tend to "broom" like spruce. Boatbuilder and author Walt Simmons, of Lincolnville, Maine, protects the tip of his oars with epoxy. He first encircles the oar's tip with a masking tape collar that extends about 1/2 inch beyond the wood, then fills the resulting reservoir with epoxy. This has proven to be more durable than metal oar tips.

Protecting the Oar

To prevent premature wear, any oar of good quality—ash or spruce—should be protected from friction with the oarlock. Plastic sleeves can be too slippery, and rubber sleeves tend to work their way up the oar and need frequent adjustment. A leathered oar is the best alternative. To obtain optimum

This beautifully leathered oar from Rivendell Marine has a long leather to protect it from wear and ease rowing. The fancywork "button" keeps the oar from slipping out accidentally should it be released.

advantage, the leathers should be kept *well lubricated* with tallow, lanolin, Mink Oil, or Vaseline.

While rubber oar stops are available and serviceable, most people who have gone to the time and expense of leathering an oar will choose a leather button as well, to keep the oar positioned in the lock. Shaw & Tenney uses 1/4-inch-thick elk hide, material an individual is unlikely to procure. A piece of leather machinery belt may be used, if available, or else a piece of 1/2-inch or 3/8-inch dacron line tacked, or preferably glued with epoxy, or, if the button is leather, a modern, resilient leather glue.

Occasionally, one sees an oar protected from chafe by tightly wrapped twine or 1/8-inch line instead of leather—either to save money or because no suitable piece of leather was available. Twine, heavily coated with varnish, makes for a nice-looking piece of antichafing gear. It won't last as long as leather, but it's not hard to apply, or replace. Some have tried coating twine with epoxy and have achieved excellent results.

Leathering an Oar

Leathering an oar confronts the dinghy owner with one of the frustrating realities of boat ownership. Advice in magazines and books, good as it is, seldom reflects the realities that confront the nonprofessional with modest resources in terms of tools and materials. Merely *buying* leather can be a major problem. "It's getting like gold, isn't it?" a friendly cobbler told me. After two weeks of searching, he managed to produce some acceptable leather for me to use on a sharpie's sprit boom. Cobblers, tanneries, and leathercraft stores are potential sources of leather, and you can check "Leather Manufacturing" in the Yellow Pages. Using two needles to produce a herringbone stitch suitable to an oar leather is described in *WoodenBoat,* Number 68. Lace the leathers—seam facing up in line with the blade to avoid wear on the stitching—instead of fastening them with tacks, which can split and eventually rot the wood.

Oarlocks

While the quest for adequate oarlocks may now bedevil connoisseurs of traditional-style pulling boats (years ago, there were dozens of intriguing patterns to choose from), it is less of a problem for the dinghy owner. What is needed, basically, is a symmetrical, horn-style lock, the socket of which may be mounted either atop or alongside the gunwale. With the limited availability of good oarlocks these days, the most frequently used kind are those with the socket set into the gunwale. These are readily available in bronze—of varying degrees of quality in terms of finish and of shaft-to-socket fit—galvanized iron, and molded nylon. Of the three, the bronze locks are the most expensive,

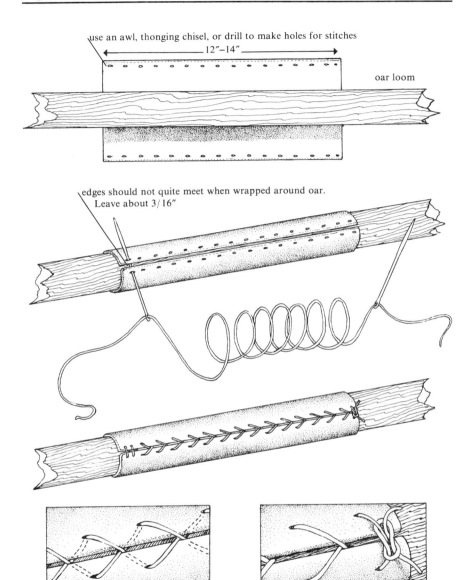

use an awl, thonging chisel, or drill to make holes for stitches

12"–14"

oar loom

edges should not quite meet when wrapped around oar.
Leave about 3/16"

Leathering an oar. (1) Wrap leather around oar and cut to size. It must fit tightly; leave about a 3/16-inch space to "draw up" when stitching. (Pete Culler suggested wetting the leather first to get a "shrink-tight" fit.) (2) Rig two sailmaker's needles with waxed twine, about 6 feet for each foot of leather. (3) Pass one needle through the leather, pulling it through until the needles are equidistant. Repeat the motion to anchor the thread. (4) Cross stitch to form a baseball-stitch pattern.

best looking, and longest lasting, although they too can bend, depending on the alloy. Once bent, an oarlock will seldom be the same again.

A good galvanized oarlock is functional enough, although most yachtsmen associate them with workboats, rust, and worn oar looms rather than with good dinghies. The nylon locks fall somewhere in between those of bronze and those of iron. They look undeniably toylike, and many people remain skeptical about them. Those who use nylon oarlocks on their boats do so primarily because of their comparatively low cost, yet even some old-timers have expressed surprise at the locks' durability. Apparently, they can last for years—if they don't break under serious abuse.

Other styles of oarlocks are also available. For a dinghy, perhaps the most useful are the circular locks that completely surround the oar. They are particularly handy when children will be using the boat, because the oars are kept from sliding out of the locks. For that reason, you cannot forget your oarlocks. Be careful when coming alongside your boat, however. I suspect that the last-minute yanking of the oar to remove it has accounted for the occasional bent shafts of circular oarlocks.

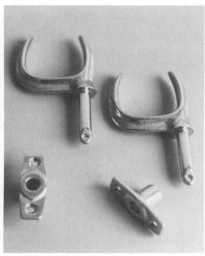

Horn-style and circular oarlocks. The latter are notably sensible in that they keep oar and lock together at all times, and, because the oarlock usually must be removed as one comes alongside, the circular locks are particularly useful for dinghies.

Seldom seen aboard dinghies, offset oarlocks permit somewhat more power throughout the full swing of the oar.

A piece of leather tacked to a plank can serve as a pocket for an oarlock, keeping it from swinging and chipping paint (or gelcoat).

Other oarlocks available to the custom or home builder include offset types, which permit greater power throughout the oar's full swing than symmetrical locks, and symmetrical locks that are oblong along the bottom, rather than circular. These lessen the tendency for an oar to rise and jump out of the socket during the stroke.

Pin-style locks, which secure the oar in place with a rod through the loom, are popular with some boatbuilders, although they may be more suitable for a fishing rowboat than a dinghy. They do secure the oar in place in the lock, permitting both to be unshipped quickly when coming alongside. They do not, however, permit an oar to be feathered, and the necessary hole through the oar's shaft inevitably weakens the wood.

Before closing this discussion of oarlocks, it might be noted that few production dinghies include a transom-mounted sculling notch or oarlock socket. Few manufacturers, it seems, consider the possibility that an oar may be lost overboard or that some buyers might simply like to learn the gentle art of sculling. For those so inclined, a sculling notch is easily added.

Small Outboards

In May 1985, the British magazine *Yachting World* published a survey in which owners rated the quality of their dinghy's outboard motor. The result ranked the brands in this order: Yamaha, Suzuki, Mariner, Johnson, Evinrude, British Seagull, and Volvo and Mercury tied. Perhaps the most noteworthy absentee from this list was Honda, whose four-stroke, 2 hp motor is highly regarded. This little survey, like one or two others of which I am aware, points to growing levels of consumer satisfaction provided by several small Japanese outboards at the expense of other established manufacturers. The British Seagull's fall from grace may be surprising to some, while others doubtless believe the motor never achieved a state of grace anyway.

The chart below shows the qualities most desirable in a dinghy outboard (although I suspect they'd be equally applicable to an outboard suitable for a daysailer or cruising sailboat) and how they may be achieved.

The perfect dinghy outboard has yet to be built. The *idea* of the British Seagull comes close, based as it is on plain bearings, a simple carburetor, and a large, low-speed propeller that is particularly well suited to pushing heavily loaded rigid dinghies. Most service points are readily accessible. But because no shroud encloses the engine, muffling the air intake, Seagulls tend to be noisy.

Furthermore, the Seagull leaves something to be desired in terms of quality. Corrosion is a problem with some parts and the dealer group, in my experience, has grown notably unenthusiastic. Still, these motors can be self-serviced fairly easily, and the current ownership of the company is, I'm told, committed to improvements. I have devoted this space to the British Seagull because, historically, the engine has been rightfully thought of as a

DINGHY OUTBOARDS

DESIRED TRAIT	NECESSARY FEATURES
Reliability—the ability to start quickly and keep running, whether after a period of idleness or under more regular use.	Simple, well-filtered fuel system; waterproof electronic ignition.
Repairability—the ability to be repaired or made to run *by an owner* of low-to-modest mechanical interest or aptitude.	Simplicity of design, few or no special tools required, clear owner's manual.
Light weight—the ability to be carried readily without undue strain.	Appropriate materials; ergonomic design, preferably with a designed-in carrying handle or convenient balance point. Air-cooled models are lighter than water-cooled ones—but noisier.
Dunkability—the ability to be made to run after being submerged. While this may be of little concern to the daysailer or coastwise cruiser, it may be of great importance to the cruiser who frequents out-of-the-way anchorages.	Plain, rather than needle, bearings; simple design requiring few or no special tools.
Quiet running.	Water cooling, lower rpm.

motor with special features applicable to dinghies. In the past several years, however, other manufacturers have paid increasing attention to the smaller outboard, and the obvious quality of several of these motors has moved them ahead of the Seagull in the marketplace.

Domestic and Japanese products, which are more complex in basic design, have ball or needle bearings on their crankshaft and connecting rods that make possible reliable operation in the 4,000-plus-rpm range and the high fuel-to-oil ratios that are typical today. The Honda, being a four-cycle engine, requires the added weight of an oil pump and the complexity of a valve train. Yet, in the very smallest displacement range, Honda's four-stroke is actually lighter than some two-strokes of comparable power, and Honda has long since proven that a four-cycle engine need not be at a disadvantage because of its valve mechanism.

No matter how handy you may be, it's good to know that parts and professional service are readily available. The domestics have comprehensive dealer networks that may be as good a reason to buy a Johnson/Evinrude or Mercury (whose 2.2 hp model is built in Japan by Tohatsu) as any combination of mechanical features. The big-name Japanese motors— Yamaha, Suzuki, Honda, Mariner—appear to have achieved much the same level of quality and customer satisfaction as Japanese automobiles.

As the size of outboards increases into the range of larger rigid dinghies or hard-transom inflatables and RIBs, the choice in outboard will be one or another of the domestic or Japanese brands. Once into the 6- to 10-hp range, manufacturer reputation and dealer service may well be the determining factor in your decision. The motors themselves are reasonably close in terms of quality, specifications, and performance.

Small Outboard Tips

For many years, a well-known paint manufacturer maintained a testing site alongside the Pennsylvania Turnpike. Here, brightly colored panels were exposed to the weather and pollutants, and their durability measured. I am reminded of those colored panels whenever I see an outboard motor clamped to the stern pulpit of a yacht. There the motor is exposed to salt, rain, and sun. An outboard maker could learn much, if such exposure testing was conducted scientifically.

An occasional freshwater rinse and wipe-down with an oily rag will help preserve an outboard. So will a canvas cover, although a tight-fitting plastic wrap may seal in moisture, doing more harm than good. Use the canvas cover no matter whether the motor is kept in a locker *or on a rail.*

Be *fastidious* about your fuel and fuel containers. Do not, even once, fill your fuel tank without using a filtered spout and a more finely filtered funnel. Battle condensation in the tank with additives and frequent fill-ups. Have your

Major outboard manufacturers do extensive research into corrosion protection and virtually all other factors relating to their outboards. When selecting an outboard, pay at least as much attention to the quality of parts and service as to the motor's features and price.

outboard serviced by the dealer from whom you bought it. Dealers routinely receive recall notices or service bulletins dealing with problems that could baffle *anyone* trying to solve a fault without them.

Whatever brand of motor you choose, resist any urge to overpower your dinghy. Extra horsepower is unlikely to get you there any sooner, particularly in a rigid dinghy with a displacement hull, but extra power may exact a significant weight penalty.

If you have a four-stroke motor, remember that you *must* occasionally check the oil level and replenish it as necessary. All outboard owners should remember to store their outboards either upright or face down. On most outboards, residual cooling water can enter the cylinders if the motor is carried or stored with the propeller higher than the cylinder.

Finally, no matter what outboard you have, don't take it for granted. Murphy's Law lurks just a few feet beyond the dock. The time you leave your oars behind will certainly be the time your otherwise-trustworthy outboard fails you. Take your oars.

Rigs, Oars, and Outboards—A Summary

- If you don't think you'll *sail* your dinghy regularly, consider saving money and simplifying the boat by not ordering the sailing version.

- If sailing ability is important to you, test-sail the dinghies in which you are interested on *all points of sailing,* preferably in a light-to-moderate breeze. Sailing dinghies should have kick-up rudders to simplify beaching and reduce the risk of inadvertently grounding, perhaps with serious consequences.

- Give serious consideration to boats equipped with sprit or lug rigs, which may offer excellent performance, together with spars easily stowed within the hull and a minimum of hardware.

- Remember that oar length is crucial to proper rowing performance and that 6 1/2 to 7 feet will be the length of oar most useful on dinghies from about 8 to 10 feet in length.

- When selecting an outboard, consider dealer service and parts availability, and remember that real value in an outboard extends well beyond purchase price.

- Always filter gasoline through a fine-mesh filter and keep your outboard motor covered when not in use. Read and retain your owner's manual.

CHAPTER FIVE

Inflatable Dinghies

*T*HERE are parts of the country, and the world, where inflatables have achieved overwhelming popularity as dinghies and, to some degree, as general fun and working boats. As a dinghy, the inflatable has much to recommend it. It is truly portable, stows compactly, and offers great stability. The better models can last for years.

However, inflatable manufacturers produce catalogs that typically focus as much on the pneumatic qualities of bikini-clad models as they do on explaining the specific features and benefits a customer should look for in an inflatable boat. Some believe customers don't need this information, and others, I suspect, would rather not get into it, because doing so would raise more questions than could comfortably be answered. There is much to understand about inflatables, however, and that's what this chapter is all about.

Unlike other small boats, the inflatable is the product not of small business but of big companies—of *industry*. It takes more than a few molds and a well-equipped small shop to produce an inflatable. The task requires textile engineers, machine-made fabrics, designers with special training, and, for several makers, electronic seam-welding machinery. Success demands high-volume sales, efficient manufacturing, widespread advertising, *and* a reliable system of dealer distribution and parts support.

When you purchase an inflatable boat, you are dealing with companies that build their dinghies and larger boats in *factories* and sell them on a worldwide scale. Achilles, the Japanese manufacturer, is an enormous conglomerate that produces plastics, shoes, automobile parts, *and* inflatable boats. Others were large tiremakers before they ever began making boats. These companies include Metzeler in West Germany, Semperit in Austria, Pirelli in Italy, and Avon, the British company that pioneered the inflatable-dinghy market in the United Kingdom and the United States.

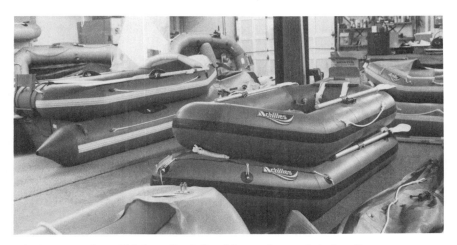

The large number of high-quality inflatables on the market gives the consumer no lack of choice. Most shops carry several brands. Before you make a decision, plan to spend some time asking pointed questions about fabric, seams, service, and warranties.

Just how difficult it is to compete in the inflatable market is perhaps best illustrated by the fact that a company as successful as Boston Whaler got out of the inflatable business after several years of effort, first with boats made for it by subcontractors in France, later with boats made in Japan. Semperit, which offered a fine line of boats, was unable to stay the course in the United States. Many others have faltered, too. When they do, it is the customer who winds up out in the cold.

About 10 years ago, some within the inflatable boat industry predicted an impending explosion of U.S. sales for inflatables. The theory was that as more and more Americans crowded into condominiums, and as water access became ever more difficult, the sales of inflatables of all types would increase, perhaps to acceptance levels rivaling those in Europe.

The explosion never came, but there has been a more or less steady growth in sales, especially those of inflatable dinghies, for which sales have risen steadily since 1978. While the inflatable dinghy has been widely accepted, the sales of larger sportboats have yet to achieve the potential the manufacturers still believe is there. Each year, however, there appears to be some growth of interest in the larger sportboats, those with inflatable keels, and the rigid inflatable boat (RIB in the industry lexicon) with fiberglass hull and fabric buoyancy tubes, Whatever the type of inflatable, manufacturers want customers to stop thinking of them as *inflatables* and start thinking of them as *boats*. This remains a battle, because many people in this country still regard inflatables as "rubber rafts," a dreaded image that continues to haunt inflatable manufacturers. Someday, the sales explosion of larger inflatable boats may occur in the United States, but I suspect that only the most patient company will be around to reap the rewards.

Inflatable yacht tenders fall into one of two categories: soft-transom models capable of absorbing up to 4 hp outboards, and hard-transom dinghies generally called *sportboats* and rated for between 6 and 8 hp. If you regularly motor distances that necessitate increased speed, the sportboat may be preferable, despite its greater cost and the potential problem of effecting a lasting joint between the wooden transom and the boat's fabric.

Some Background

Although some within the industry claim to be the inventors of inflatable boats, such claims invariably exaggerate the truth. As a consumer, you need not be concerned with who *invented* the inflatable boat, just who is building the best model to suit your needs and budget. While existing companies may have pioneered modern inflatables, the idea has been around for a long time. A 2,500-year-old stone plaque in the British Museum, for instance, shows swimmers supported by inflated skins. In the seventh century B.C., the Assyrians built rafts supported by inflated hides.

In the early 1920s, Abercrombie and Fitch sold an inflatable boat designed and built by the chief engineer of a Hammondsport, New York, blimpmaker named Airships, Inc. This boat was made of pieces cut from rubberized fabric. The parts were glued and sewn together and the joints were taped over twice and glued again. The boats were available in 7-, 8-, and 10-foot lengths. Boats like this were carried by Admiral Richard Byrd on a transatlantic flight to Europe, and by Charles Lindbergh in the *Spirit of St. Louis.* Lindbergh wrote that he saw a "black rubber raft . . . in the window of a sporting-goods store," and bought it.

It was a French company, however, that made a more concerted effort to develop the inflatable as a serious piece of boating equipment. Société Zodiac was founded in Paris in 1908 to build airships. The company manufactured such craft during World War I, and later, when airship disasters pretty much ended the future for lighter-than-air craft, Zodiac engineers began investigating alternative uses for the silk fabric that would no longer be turned into blimps. In 1934, a two-place kayak was introduced, followed two years later by an outboard-powered catamaran.

With these boats as a basis, the company began to grow. Today Zodiac employs more than 2,000 people worldwide, many of them at its main factory in Rochefort-sur-Mer, to produce its boats, which have found wide acceptance among yachtsmen as well as among many navies.

During the last 30 years, the inflatable dinghy as we know it today began to become a factor in the boating world, as more and more manufacturers

"Rubber rafts" of World War II. These workmen are putting the finishing touches to inflatables at the Goodyear factory in 1942.

How they make them. This is an overall view of the Avon factory, where inflatable boats are built the old-fashioned way of hypalon-coated nylon with hand-glued seams.

entered the field. Avon pioneered the inflatable dinghy market in the United Kingdom and North America, exhibiting its first dinghies, 8- and 12-footers, in 1960. Production first began in an old woolen mill. Today the boats are built in a modern factory in Wales by some 500 people, and Avon has become one of Great Britain's leading exporters of marine products.

The basis of an inflatable boat is the fabric of which it is made, the materials with which that fabric is coated, and the method by which the elements are joined together. It would be hard to overemphasize the importance of fabric, coating, and construction; they are the factors that determine how long a boat will last, how easy it will be to repair, and how much it will cost.

If one were to compare a high-priced fiberglass dinghy with a moderately priced version after several years of use, both hulls, at least, should be sound and sturdy. Compare different grades of inflatables, however, and the results may be more dramatic. The more expensive boat should exhibit little or no wear. The less costly boat may be leaking air or literally falling apart at the seams, or its fabric may be showing through where the coating has been chafed away or been broken down by ultraviolet radiation and ozone.

Reinforced Fabric

During the 1920s and early 1930s, inflatables were made of natural fabrics such as cotton, linen, and jute. The fabric was coated with natural rubber and, depending on conditions and the care they received, such boats could last for years. But natural rubber is adversely affected by both ozone and ultraviolet rays, and natural fabrics are subject to deterioration by moisture and mildew.

In 1938, DuPont introduced nylon, a new synthetic material that, among other things, changed the nature of inflatable-boat technology. When coated with neoprene synthetic rubber, nylon cloth became a good material with which to make inflatable boats, and it led to the mass production of survival rafts and dinghies. During World War II, such boats performed well, and it was not uncommon to hear stories of men set adrift in their rafts after ditching their airplanes.

Among the most famous of these stories involved a chief petty officer named Harold Dixon and the two-man crew of his torpedo bomber. They found themselves adrift in a five-year-old Goodyear-built dinghy that, "with its sides inflated like tires, . . . resembled an oblong donut. The dimensions were eighty inches by forty inches. . . . Occasionally, I would touch up any frayed spots where it looked as if the fabric might be weakening." The trio survived a 1,000-mile, 34-day drift without oars and finally made a landfall. Later the same year, Eddie Rickenbacker and the crew of a downed B-17 survived aboard rafts for 21 days.

There have been many developments in fabric and coating materials since then, but nylon remained the basis of the best-quality boats until challenged,

This Goodyear-built dinghy was the boat in which Navy Chief Harold Dixon and the crew of his scout bomber, Tony Pastula and Gene Aldrich, survived a 34-day Pacific ordeal in 1942. The men were decorated by Admiral Chester Nimitz and their story was skillfully told in Robert Trumbull's The Raft.

beginning in the late 1960s, by polyester fabrics. The physical properties of polyesters and nylons are similar in many respects, but those who use polyester cite increased resistance to ultraviolet rays, a lower degree of elongation (stretch) than nylon under similar circumstances and loads, reduced cost, and—perhaps most important—a compatibility with plastomer (PVC) coatings rather than elastomers such as hypalon. It is *that* difference, as we'll see, that is critical to the method of joining the boat's seams.

Whatever the fabric, its strength depends in part on its weight, which is generally expressed in deniers or, more recently, decitex. Whether the measure is denier or decitex, each refers to the weight of a single strand of thread of a specified length. The higher the denier, the thicker the filaments that make up the fabric. Thread weights were standardized years ago by textile mills. Most inflatable dinghies, whether nylon or polyester, use 420-, 840-, and 1,000-denier fabrics. Typically, price variations within a manufacturer's model line relate to the weight of the fabric being used. You can assume that the more the boat costs, the heavier duty it is and the longer it will last.

Denier alone, however, is not an adequate indication of a boat's probable

*An oar for a mast, an oar for a rudder. So equipped, this Goodyear raft
(photographed in December 1943) could sail downwind, rather than merely drift.*

strength, for strength depends on many interrelated factors. It would be too
simplistic, for example, to suggest that by gluing two layers of 840-denier
material together, a 1,680-denier material results, with twice the strength of the
originally quoted rating.

In fact, the weight and strength of fabric are predicated on many factors,
including the number of yarns per inch, the type of weave, the sizing or
treatment given the yarn, and even the machine used for weaving. Strength
also depends in part on how the fabric is coated and with what. Generally
speaking, higher-denier fabrics have higher tear figures than lower denier
fabrics. Yet such figures do not tell the whole story, either. When fabric is torn,
its threads often bunch up, which means that several threads at a time are
being torn and an artificially high strength figure may emerge. This bunching
effect is worsened if coating-to-fabric adhesion is poor, and higher-denier
fabrics generally *do* have lower rubber-to-fabric adhesion qualities. Nor can a
thick coating make up for the strength lacking in an overly light or loosely

woven fabric. Bottom line: If you *really* want to know what the manufacturer thinks of its fabric, check the warranty.

While denier is related to fabric strength, it also affects a fabric's "wicking" qualities. Wicking is the tendency of air to travel along the base fabric and seep out through the coating. Higher-denier fabrics often allow more air to leak out along their thicker threads, so a boat with a higher denier rating may need to be topped off with air more often than one made of somewhat lighter-weight material.

Inflatable technology is the province of the textile engineer and the chemist. Not only is it a highly specialized subject but it is complicated further by the accelerating changes within the industry during the past several years. Those involve a move, by some manufacturers, away from "traditional" nylon fabrics impregnated with hypalon and glued together by hand, to boats made of PVC-coated polyester fabric with the seams fused electronically. In both cases, however, the boats are built of reinforced fabric, woven material to which a coating is bonded or impregnated to render the fabric largely airtight.

Unreinforced Fabric

The far less costly alternative to woven fabric, whether nylon or polyester, is polyvinyl chloride (PVC). It depends for its strength on thickness and the plastifiers or resins in the material itself. PVC is inherently stretchy, by comparison to supported fabric, and invariably is used for automated manufacture with heat-sealed seams. Boats built of PVC may have more in common with swimming-pool toys than heavy-duty dinghies. However, there are some PVC boats that may be entirely satisfactory, thanks to reliable fabric, good design, and adequate chambering. Given their low cost, such dinghies may well fit the needs of many on tight budgets who understand they are buying something intended for light-duty use as a tender, or camping or fishing on protected waters.

Coatings

Since World War II, developments involving nylon fabrics have centered on improving coating materials. In the late 1940s, for instance, a French manufacturer named Hutchinson-Mapa was using styrene-butadiene rubber (SBR). It was superior to natural rubber but still subject to ultraviolet and ozone breakdown, which varied in severity depending on where the boat was used. When Hutchinson-Mapa adopted a new synthetic rubber, matters improved dramatically. The new material was called hypalon, and it, too, had been developed by DuPont, which first offered it for sale in 1951.

Recalling Hutchinson-Mapa's adoption of hypalon, one of the company's directors told *DuPont Magazine,* "We'd been hearing quite a lot about 'Hypalon' synthetic rubber and its remarkable ability to withstand the effects of ozone and UV radiation, not to mention its excellent resistance to abrasion, oils and many chemicals. So we obtained some of the elastomer for intensive testing."

Since its introduction, hypalon has been used for such things as coating heavy-duty electrical cables, the handrails of escalators, flexible fuel-storage tanks, and air-supported canopies over convertible swimming pool/skating rinks. To increase its flexibility and adhesion to the base fabric of a boat, hypalon usually is mixed with neoprene and quantities of other materials. A good-quality hypalon coating will contain about 80 percent hypalon. A more modest amount will cost a manufacturer less money, but will substantially reduce a boat's quality.

Hypalon is supplied by DuPont in pellet form and applied to the base fabric either by spreading or, as in most high-quality inflatables, by a process known as calendering. Calendered fabric is passed through heavy rollers, which impregnate the weave with the coating material. At Avon, one pass through the rollers suffices for both sides, and Avon is among the few manufacturers to use hypalon both inside the tubes and out. Others coat the inside with neoprene, a material that tends to be more airtight than hypalon. Some of those who sell competing brands report that the neoprene-coated boats require less topping-off after a week on the showroom floor. This is not necessarily a functional advantage, however, and a need for somewhat more frequent topping-off has no relation to a boat's longevity.

The primary alternative to nylon fabric coated with hypalon and/or neoprene is polyester fabric coated with polyvinyl chloride. This has been referred to as "the wave of the future," and Zodiac led the way in its use. It combines the advantageous physical properties of polyester with these further advantages: (1) PVC is somewhat less expensive to handle than hypalon, since it need not be mixed in individual batches. (2) PVC can be compounded in virtually any color. (3) Perhaps most important, the seams of a polyester/PVC boat can be welded electronically, saving production time and thus helping, in theory, to minimize cost increases.

Seams

Boats built of hypalon/neoprene-coated nylon are generally constructed by hand and glued together with special adhesives in a labor-intensive process that accounts, in part, for their comparatively high cost. The process is referred to as cold-gluing or cold-vulcanization. Heat is not necessary to the process. At Avon, which continues to use this method, boats are built as follows: The coated fabric is positioned on a 30-foot-long cutting table and a die slices out the various shapes. The edges of the panels are then passed through a buffing machine to roughen the surfaces that will adhere to each other. Next, the pieces are placed on an assembly jig and overlapping sections are glued together with a two-part adhesive (mixed fresh daily). The glue is stronger in its bond than the fabric itself, yet it permits ungluing for repairs merely by applying the heat of a hair-dryer–like device.

Constructing a boat in this fashion is not an assembly-line process. Making an airtight tube in a subdivided boat, for instance, requires time and skill. Panels are first joined so that the tube assumes the shape of a long ribbon of material. Next, internal baffles are fitted to separate the chambers. Then the main seam is closed. Skillful workmanship is also required to join the various overlapping seams, which may vary from 1 to 2 inches in width. Some panels containing complex curves need to be joined to comparatively straight panels, and this must be done to avoid creating wrinkles or creases when inflated. There is a curing time of 24 hours for the glued joints, and when they are dry, each chamber is tested on a manometer, a device that converts the air pressure within the tube to water pressure on a graduated 54-inch-long scale. The gauge reveals whether the tube's airtightness is up to standard.

The essentially handmade nature of construction like this means there may be slight differences in boats of the same model. In terms of dinghies, the differences are not likely to affect performance in any significant way. Those who regularly handle higher-powered sportboats, however, say that such differences occasionally may require the fitting of a different propeller to achieve identical performance levels. Critics of the process refer to it as "labor-intensive and subject to human error. Limited production. Closed technology."

All of that may be argued, but cold-glued dinghies and larger craft built of nylon-coated hypalon unquestionably have proved their durability. Twelve-year-old Avons can be found standing inflated, exposed to the weather, in yacht harbors throughout the United Kingdom. The survival of Maurice and Maralyn Bailey, adrift in the Pacific for 117 days with an Avon liferaft and a Redcrest dinghy, is an epic of modern-day sea survival. The Avon company's newspaper takes obvious delight in publishing accounts related by happy owners. Several years ago, *Avon Expedition News,* which is primarily devoted to the experiences of adventurers and explorers, included a little article about a man who had been using his Redstart dinghy for 16 years, towing it in "all weathers through many Scottish lochs and firths."

For many years, Zodiac boats were built with similar cold-glued methods. It was in a 15-foot Zodiac that French doctor Alain Bombard drifted and sailed across the Atlantic in 1952, eating plankton and stretching freshwater supplies by also drinking modest amounts of sea water. Bombard's was a controversial passage, and remains so to this day, but it proved the capability of the Zodiac, among other things. Later, Bombard became an adviser to the firm of Angevinière, which introduced the Bombard line of inflatable dinghies and larger craft. No longer, however, are these boats built the same way as

One of the "old black ones." Photographed in 1979, this early Avon Redstart had served its owner well. Avon's slogan—"When You Consider Cost, Consider Value"—remains as true today as it was when this little boat was first sold.

Bombard's *L'Hérétique* or the top-line Zodiac models of the late 1970s. Instead, they are built of PVC-coated polyester with welded seams.

The development of the PVC-coated polyester fabrics has resulted in a clear division, and conflicting claims, between those who continue to build boats using hypalon-coated nylon fabrics with overlapping cold-glued seams, and the PVC boats with fused seams, a technique often referred to as thermo-bonding. The latter is by far the quicker process, and even though raw-materials costs are about the same, labor costs are reduced dramatically, by half or even more. In a market subject to the potential pressures of both monetary inflation and currency fluctuation, that difference in labor cost can sometimes help stabilize prices.

Cold-Glued Nylon/Hypalon versus Thermo-Bonded Polyester/PVC

Some 10 years ago, when the first edition of *The Dinghy Book* was published, it noted that "like any 'wave of the future,' the polyester/PVC onslaught has not been without some teething problems." Even proponents of PVC admit that it does not have the abrasion resistance of hypalon. Some PVC boats subjected to the rigors of whitewater rafting developed failures, including leaking air chambers, parting of the heat-welded seams, and delamination of the fabric in much-abused areas such as the floor. Extreme exposure to gas/oil mixtures, which leaves nylon/hypalon unaffected, is likely to make PVC-coated polyester brittle.

One comparison of the two materials was conducted in France by the fabric-manufacturing firm of Pennel and Flipo. The tests showed the hypalon-coated fabric to have significantly better UV stability and greater resistance to gas and oil. The former was reflected in the greater resistance to fading of hypalon, the latter by the tendency of PVC fabric to become stiff, while the hypalon-coated material remained pleasantly flexible.

An informal 1988 survey of a half-dozen inflatable repair centers suggests that all is not yet ideal with the newer technology. The most commonly cited problems were transom separation in sportboats and the great difficulty of making lasting repairs to PVC-coated hulls. The problems appeared more extreme in areas like Florida and the Caribbean than in more moderate zones. Said one experienced repairman in the Virgin Islands, "The polyester fabric does fine up north, but down here patches tear off and transoms come loose. We just don't see that problem with the nylon/hypalon cold-glued boats."

In terms of the transoms, the problem is one of gluing a wooden part to PVC-coated fabric, not a difficult thing to do with a hypalon/nylon boat, but apparently *very* difficult when PVC is involved. Inflatable service specialists also point out that repairs to PVC-coated boats must be carried out within a specific range of temperature and humidity—a limitation that doesn't affect hypalon/nylon models. That can be a consideration if one is using a dinghy primarily in tropical areas. One repairman noted that, much to his surprise, the repaired transoms of some PVC boats appeared more secure than when the boat was delivered from the factory.

The debate between makers of the cold-glued models and boats with heat-sealed seams is unlikely to diminish any time soon. In the very front of its catalog, the French maker Sillinger claims its cold-gluing gives "much higher strength and safety guarantees. . . . Nowadays, most professional users, including the French Navy, require inflatable boats assembled with this technology, which necessitates a highly skilled labour force since all glued seams are fully hand made."

Achilles, which ranks as one of the largest producers of PVC-coated materials in the world, but builds its boats of nylon fabric coated on the inside with neoprene and on the outside with hypalon, also is outspoken in its criticism.

Zodiac, on the other hand, claims its trademarked Strongan PVC-coated fabrics are tomorrow's technology and offer higher resistance to chafing, greater airtightness, better UV resistance, and longer life. At the same time, the company currently uses cold-glued nylon and nylon/Kevlar fabric in its larger models. Zodiac now owns Bombard and Metzeler as well, and today builds these models with the same methods and materials as the Zodiac label boats.

Design

If many fiberglass dinghies tend to look alike, the same can be said for inflatables, although for different reasons. Some are U-shaped at each end. Most have V-shaped bows with gently rounded corners and U-shaped sterns. It's a shape that hasn't changed much in almost 50 years, yet manufacturers still experiment. A company like Avon has a warehouse full of boats never produced—boats with, for example, 3 inches of lift to the bow, or 8 inches, to test how much drier such a design might be, or how much it is affected by wind. Designers experiment with extra panels here and there to test rigidity. Tube diameters are changed to determine the effect on performance and stability. Tube diameter also has an important effect on torsional rigidity: When the tube doubles in diameter, its stiffness increases fourfold.

The accompanying chart provides a comparison of three popular dinghies.

THE "BIG THREE" INFLATABLES

	ACHILLES LT-4DX	AVON REDCREST	ZODIAC T 280
Length overall	9 ft. 5 in.	9 ft. 3 in.	9 ft. 2 in.
Length inside	7 ft. 1 in.	6 ft. 10 in.	6 ft. 7 in.
Beam overall	4 ft. 7 in.	4 ft. 6 in.	4 ft. 11 in.
Beam inside	2 ft. 3 in.	2 ft. 4 in.	2 ft. 4 in.
Tube diameter	14.2 in.	15 in.	16 in.
Capacity:			
Weight/Persons	990 lb./4	700 lb./4	882 lb./4
No. air chambers	4	2+ thwart	2 (thwart opt.)
Weight w/flrbrds	65 lb.*	67 lb.	51 lb.
Floorboards	Plywood panels, roll-up type	Plywood panels or roll-up slats	Plywood slats, roll-up type
Construction	Nylon/hypalon/ neoprene, glued	Nylon/hypalon, glued	Polyester/PVC, thermo-bonding

*includes wooden stern seat and motor mount

The chart makes interesting reading, if only because it reveals how similar these dinghies are in many respects. The somewhat greater size of the Achilles, and the Zodiac's wide beam and large tube diameter, result in higher load capacities than in the Avon, although no uniform standards for measuring load capacities currently are in use. Generally, a boat will be loaded up to, but not over, its antichafe strip, after which a "safety factor" will be added in and a load figure decided upon. All of these dinghies, however, offer greater weight-carrying capacities than one is ever likely to approach, given the amount of space available within their interior dimensions.

With their narrower beams and smaller-diameter tubes, the Avon and the

Achilles could be expected to be somewhat better performers than the Zodiac, and less affected by the wind. Both the Avon and the Achilles have a stern seat, unavailable on the Zodiac. Getting a passenger's weight off the rear or side buoyancy tube can only help an inflatable's performance under oars.

As the chart shows, perhaps the biggest difference between the "Big Three" remains their materials and construction. But that is a major consideration, and it is one reflected in warranty coverage, which is as follows:

1988 WARRANTY INFORMATION

	FABRIC	SEAMS	PARTS	TRANSOM
Achilles	5 yr.	5 yr.	90 da.	1 yr.
Avon	10 yr.	5 yr.	1 yr.	1 yr.
Zodiac	5 yr.	5 yr.	90 da.	1 yr.

The subject of warranty coverage raises the question of service. The world's inflatable manufacturers view the U.S. market as a vast one, theoretically far more lucrative than their own. But when you buy a boat, you must rely on the maker to *stay in the market* if you are to get warranty service or parts. As already noted, however, the field is crowded with those who have come and gone. With the Big Three, at least, the purchaser can be fairly certain that he won't be left to fend for himself when a warranty claim arises. Developing a relationship with a dealer, rather than buying by mail, may be one way to protect yourself further in this regard. Zodiac and Avon have generally earned a good reputation in terms of warranty service.

How Big Should an Inflatable Be?

Because so much of an inflatable's volume is filled by the buoyancy tubes, there is surprisingly little space left for people and gear. Before buying a boat under 9 feet in length, note that a 9-footer, which is capable of carrying four people, is already cramped with two persons and a boat bag, or two people and a small cooler. Depending on your needs, a smaller model could be very inconvenient.

Floorboards

Floorboards are almost as important to optimized performance as is proper inflation. It doesn't take much imagination to picture the hydrodynamic disaster represented by an inflatable without floorboards. Wherever a foot or piece of gear rests on the bottom fabric, a protrusion will form underwater. Floorboards streamline the boat's bottom and add some weight, which doesn't hurt either. Not using floorboards would negate a large part of the reason for owning a hard-transom dinghy with its more powerful motor. Without them, the motor must push a lumpy bottom, in essence a *fouled bottom.*

Floorboards have their downside, unfortunately. They detract greatly from an inflatable's portability. Therefore, unless the boat is to remain inflated for longer than a day's use, the performance penalty represented by their absence is almost certain to count for little. Because floorboards fit tightly between the buoyancy chambers and the floor fabric, chafe is a potential problem in this hard-to-reach area. Good boats usually have extra fabric in the floor/buoyancy chamber area, however. The biggest enemy is sand. Trapped between the floorboards and the fabric, or even just between the floor fabric and the buoyancy tubes, sand can act like sand*paper* and damage this portion of any inflatable. Care when assembling the boat, and frequent hosing with fresh water, is called for to reduce the chance of damage.

The dinghies listed earlier in the chart are supplied with a variety of floorboard types, typically plywood panels or wooden slats. The slats offer an advantage in terms of portability, but the overall stiffness of a solid floor provides the ultimate in performance.

The expanse of a varnished plywood floor can be treacherously slippery when wet, and an inflatable's tendency to scoot out from underfoot unless well restrained only complicates this problem when boarding. For that reason, consider painting the area *not* in contact with the buoyancy chambers with paint to which nonskid material has been added. Nonskid can be added to varnish, so a thorough sanding of the floorboards can be followed by application of nonskid varnish, if you prefer varnish to paint.

Inflatable Floors

Of the higher-quality inflatables, only the Metzeler offers inflatable floor tubes. These have always seemed to me to offer advantages, providing a fair bottom, extra flotation, and performance-enhancing overall stiffness. Of course, the floor tubes represent the potential for increased leaks, and it is crucial to exercise even more care than normal when beaching such boats. It was Metzeler's inflatable-floor technology that has been cited as an important reason for the company's purchase by Zodiac. Thus far, however, inflatable floors have not proven to be enough of either a performance advance or a selling feature for other manufacturers to develop.

Thwarts

There is not much to be said, one way or the other, about the different types of seats used in inflatable dinghies. The most common arrangement is an inflatable rowing seat, although several boats are equipped with wooden seats.

An inflatable thwart adds buoyancy—115 pounds' worth, according to Avon. Such thwarts work fine and add rigidity to the hull as long as they are fully inflated. Sitting on a squishy pillow of a thwart does nothing to help the rowing qualities of an inflatable dinghy. That is not a problem with a wooden thwart, of course, but the latter must be attached to the hull by some means, and if it is bonded, it represents a potential service headache at some point.

The thwart of an inflatable will place you in some sort of relation to the oarlocks, but it won't be a position much like the arrangement in a hard dinghy or rowing boat. Instead, the angle at which the oars enter the water—which depends largely on tube diameter and where the oarlocks are mounted on the tubes—may seem odd. There's nothing you can do to change the boat, however, so it's a case of adapting.

Watch Out For the Fittings

Inflatables are often cited as being "easy on topsides" when lying alongside other boats. This is largely true. However, the black-rubber fittings can leave lasting streaks and marks, particularly on wooden boats with soft, flat-finish paint. Care should also be taken to keep metal tow rings from contacting the side of the hull. In many cases, it will make sense to put out a fender.

Oarlocks and Oars

Inflatable-boat oarlocks fall into two general categories: the molded rubber "block" used by Avon and all the rest. The latter include various types of metal or nylon/plastic combinations of sockets and horns. Doubtless, there is something good about all of them, but a specific type of oarlock hardware forever limits you to that type only. Unless you invent a way to modify things, you will need to replace a broken part with an identical one, and are likely to be limited to using only the manufacturer's oars. The Avon oarlock can accept a variety of oars, and can even be fitted with a wooden mount you devise in order to install your own oarlocks.

Chances are that the oars will be supplied with your boat and that they will be whatever length and style the manufacturer deems best. Five- and 6-foot-long oars are typical, although short oars and large-diameter tubes cause the oars to enter the water at a steep, uncomfortable angle. Two-piece oars, either wood or aluminum, seem to be the rule, mostly because they stow so compactly. If you have the choice, and the room to stow them, consider adding a pair of the longest practical solid oars to your inventory. They greatly reduce the chance of an oar's breaking at the joint—which should be inspected for rot or fatigue from time to time—and you can buy them in longer lengths

A well-equipped Avon Redcrest. A stern seat and bow dodger are useful accessories, the latter of particular value in keeping things dry when motoring. Note that the interior space of even a 9-foot inflatable is quickly filled. Rowing performance can be enhanced by using longer oars than the standard-equipment 5 1/2-footers.

than those supplied with the boat, thus increasing performance. In my experience, the Avon-type two-piece oars are entirely satisfactory for light-duty use. No matter what sort of oars you use, however, remove them or secure them very well when you are going to tow your dinghy.

Inflation

Getting the best out of an inflatable primarily involves keeping it inflated properly and keeping it clean. Many owners are afraid to pump up their boats adequately, fearing a seam might burst. Yet, those who sell and service inflatable dinghies report that seam leakage caused by too much air pressure is almost never a problem with good-quality dinghies. For most dinghies, the bursting point of the tubes is at least four times higher than the recommended inflation pressure. However, if you inflate a boat during the cooler hours of the day, it is often helpful to release some air as the temperature rises, thus reducing stress.

Underinflation results in a less-than-rigid structure that will neither row nor motor as the boat's designers intended. So make sure that all the air chambers—and especially the inflatable thwart, if your boat has one—are inflated properly. An inflatable's rowing performance may not be the greatest, but proper inflation will help you get the best from your boat.

How long it takes to inflate and deflate a dinghy is likely to have a major influence on your satisfaction with it. Because it is not easy to modify or change the valves in an inflatable, you'll have to live with the valve with which the boat is equipped. All-plastic valves are corrosion-proof and, if of adequate dimension, make short work of inflation and deflation (providing the pump is a good one).

Metal valves offer the potential for corrosion, and metal/plastic valves with threaded caps may lead to the cross-threading of the softer plastic material. In my experience, the high-capacity pump supplied with Avon boats, which has a reasonably comfortable "heel angle," is an excellent device, as is the Avon valve.

Maintenance

The basic maintenance of inflatables involves, first of all, awareness. The less you drag your boat, the more willing you are to get your feet wet when launching from and landing on a beach, the longer the bottom fabric will last. When its coating wears thin and the bottom becomes porous, replacement of the bottom fabric will probably be necessary. Glued-on bottom patches can protect the fabric somewhat. Be aware, too, of anything that can chafe the buoyancy tubes.

If you regularly tow the boat, make sure the towing bridle—which divides towing stresses over *two* fittings rather than a bow ring alone, and enhances straight-line towing—doesn't rub directly against the tubes. If it does, slip a piece of plastic tubing over the bridle.

Periodic washing with fresh water will help maintain the boat's appearance, but be sure to let the boat dry thoroughly if it is to be stored after washing. Otherwise, hard-to-remove mildew stains can result. Installed floorboards should be removed monthly so that sand and dirt can be thoroughly hosed away.

There are some, perhaps many, inflatable owners who treat their boats to periodic cleaning with a polymer substance containing silicone. Such chemicals impart a shiny "finish" to plastic and rubber and can maintain or restore a pleasing, "like-new" look. However, once those polymers get thoroughly embedded in the fabric, they are difficult to remove and can greatly complicate the otherwise-straightforward business of gluing on a patch. Virtually every inflatable repair shop with which I spoke mentioned this problem. Some noted further that repeated use of the product might contribute to the breakdown of glued seams. They have the additional property of making the boat unpleasantly slippery.

Soap and water, or such cleaners as 409 or Fantastik, should be all that is necessary for an inflatable boat. Recently, a nonsilicone cleaner/restorer called 303, developed by Ameritech Industries of Redding, California, was introduced to the marine market. Originally developed for use in the aerospace industry, 303 contains an ultraviolet screen and appears to be an excellent restorative and protective material for use on inflatables, as well as on sailcloth and unwaxed fiberglass surfaces. The material currently is under consideration by some manufacturers as a final finish on new inflatables. (Note that inflatables regularly stored on deck can be protected from UV rays by a fitted dacron, not nylon, cover.)

Of Mice and Boats

Inflatables should be stored *dry;* talcum powder sprinkled on the boat can help act as a drying agent. If possible, save the original carton in which your boat was delivered. Put the folded boat in its bag and store it in the carton to discourage rodents from gnawing the fabric. Store the boat in a dry place, off the floor if possible.

Summary and Recommendations

- Buying an inflatable is much like buying a car. Try to buy from an experienced dealer who will stand, and *has stood,* behind the boat, should it need warranty work, routine service, or parts.

- Remember that even a well-meaning dealer can be left out in the cold by a manufacturer. When making a purchase decision, consider the manufacturer's past record in this country.

- No matter what boat you are buying, check with an experienced repair shop or two.

- Remember that in inflatables, as in almost everything else, there are few, if any, bargains. You still get what you pay for.

- Keep your boat well inflated for optimal performance, and don't allow sand to remain for long between the floor fabric and the buoyancy tubes, especially if floorboards are fitted.

- If you will regularly be motoring, the added performance of a hard transom may well be worthwhile, and those who can store a dinghy aboard in davits or elsewhere might find a rigid inflatable boat (RIB) can best meet their needs.

CHAPTER SIX

In the Water

*I*F YOU read enough tales of yachts lost either offshore or onshore, the dinghy's prominent role in deciding the outcome of such experiences soon becomes evident. Most of those who live to write or tell about these ordeals find their dinghies wanting, and pay *far closer* attention thereafter to the selection and care of a tender. If there is one recurrent theme that runs through such stories, it is of the inadequate design and construction of altogether too many dinghies. As can be seen from the following true anecdotes, the errors in judgment most of us make at one time or another handling our very small boats are a more common problem.

ON a calm late-summer night, a Stone Horse sloop lies to her anchor just outside the Essex River, west of Gloucester, Massachusetts. The skipper hears a muffled cry for help from somewhere across the dark, still water. Hearing things? No, there it is again.

Together with his companion, he sets out in his 8-foot fiberglass dinghy, powered by a brand-new 2 hp Evinrude, purchased to drive the dinghy against the combined force of the tide and river from their anchorage in the bay up to Essex. Now, the motor speeds them toward a man in trouble.

It is an older man, clinging, more or less, to his cabin cruiser; growing weaker and colder over time, unable to climb aboard. The rescuers reach him before it is too late and the shivering man is helped aboard.

"I was untying my dinghy," he tells them, "and somehow it got away. I thought I could catch it, if I jumped in after it, but I couldn't. And then I couldn't climb aboard." Abashed, embarrassed, and thankful, the man buys his rescuers dinner the following evening. Over wine, he admits that he is a retired Coast Guard officer.

ON a clear day, a sturdy steel ketch departs Bermuda for the Bahamas. Before long, the vessel is caught up in a hurricane and sinks. The four men in the crew abandon ship, and after some 12 hours in the water, manage to bail out and then board their 8-foot fiberglass dinghy. (The ketch's liferaft had been blown away in its container.) Oars and oarlocks are in the boat, but nothing else. Two-and-a-half days after the sinking, the men are rescued by a passing ship.

IT is past midnight on Long Island Sound. A gaff-rigged sloop scurries eastward. Her owner, sensing an ominous change in the breeze, leaves his inexperienced companion at the tiller and moves forward to reduce sail. Out of the darkness, a white squall pounces. The crewman is unable to follow orders. Instead of luffing into the wind, he falls off, sheet cleated. The skipper struggles to lower the sails but a halyard jams. Even as the skipper reaches the cabin to grab an axe or a knife, the cockpit fills and the sloop begins to sink. There is nothing left to do except haul in the plunging dinghy and board it. The yacht disappears beneath the waves. The dinghy has no oars aboard. The two men drift helplessly until rescued sometime the following day.

A FAMILY, out for a day's sail, drops its mooring and heads out. Their dinghy trails too far astern, however, and their towline fouls another boat's mooring buoy. Pulled to a halt. the family's sailboat begins to drift out of control. Everyone in the world is watching.

ON a day just before the onset of winter a shallow-draft powerboat skims across New Jersey's Barnegat Bay, The boat, recently purchased, suffers a structural failure and sinks in the frigid water. With no dinghy to offer refuge, one of the two men aboard, tragically, does not make it to shore.

IN the Caribbean, a 32-foot cutter strikes a floating object and skipper Peter Tangvald is forced to abandon ship in a dinghy that "was just seven feet long and of flimsy plywood construction." Creating a jury rig of oars and an awning is complicated by the absence of a knife, but Tangvald, a self-avowed lucky fellow, sails his little boat some 55 miles to safety, telling himself that his next dinghy will be larger and be equipped with a sailing rig.

A 35-FOOT sailboat approaches a dock under power, dinghy trailing astern. The skipper engages reverse and guns the engine. There is a sudden silence. He looks over the transom to where the towline has fouled the propeller, and then at the dock, now slowly receding as he drifts with no control.

THIS is not a book about sea survival, and these brief stories of disaster are included only to underscore how critical a dinghy can be to your safety. And this is true whether you sail offshore or are merely cruising coastwise, especially after the boating season has ended, when the water is cold and few other boats are out. For the great majority of recreational boaters, dinghy handling will involve safely launching and retrieving the boat, towing it, and handling it under oars, outboard power, or sail. Even so, safety should be *foremost* in your mind, for you are more likely to have a fright rowing an overloaded dinghy in a choppy harbor than while sailing or powering the larger boat that brought you there.

The Dinghy and the U.S. Coast Guard

In August 1978, the Coast Guard enacted level-flotation guidelines that remain in effect today. These guidelines are applicable to boats less than 20 feet long and intended for use with an engine, oars, or paddles. Sailboats and sailing dinghies are unaffected by the guidelines, and certifying one would, in fact, be a technical violation of the rules. However, any dinghy rated for more than 2 hp must, when swamped, support 50 percent of its rated passenger weight, and it must remain in an upright, level position. Before the new regulation, the swamped boat merely had to float.

"Usually, they'd roll over on their backs at about a 45-degree angle with only the bow eye out," said a Coast Guard safety expert, "and we found people would try to swim ashore but then drown. The new rule sought to instill confidence in people to remain with the boat."

Coast Guard certification plates like this, or the optional yellow stickers, carry the boat's official rating for engine horsepower, number of persons, and weight. Give some thought to how much weight you will carry and try to get some idea of how your dinghy will handle when loaded to capacity.

A boat that meets level-flotation guidelines can be expected to support its passengers with the water inside the hull at about waist level. Dinghies certified for 2 hp or less, or for oars only, must meet less stringent requirements. They must support *only 2/15* of their rated capacity, remaining upright while the crew, in the water, clings to the gunwales. Note that a boat that will support its crew and allow them to bail it out when swamped, offers a significant advantage over other models. Some dinghy manufacturers go out of their way to stress the safety of their boats, and their stories are worth serious consideration.

Whatever engine rating a dinghy carries, each boat must carry a prominently displayed yellow-and-black capacity sticker stating the maximum weight of people and gear recommended by the builder, and the maximum horsepower. If it doesn't carry the boat's serial number and a statement noting that the craft complies with the Coast Guard's requirements, another plate must be affixed that does so. Such plates were supposed to be resistant to weathering, but when it became obvious that metal plates deteriorated, an "Amendment to Capacity Information Label on Boats" was passed in 1980. It requires a bright yellow background, which typically results in a printed stick-on label that is reasonably resistant to fading.

Although boating fatality statistics do not reflect whether a dinghy or a larger boat was involved, fatalities have dropped significantly since the level-flotation guidelines were enacted. The grim number was 9.8 fatalities per 100,000 boats in 1978 but was 6.1 per 100,000 midway through 1988. "We feel," said a Coast Guard spokesman, "that level flotation has contributed to the decrease, because it gives a stable platform from which to rescue people."

According to the Coast Guard, most small-craft manufacturers go out of their way to meet the level-flotation guidelines. The Coast Guard gives the majority of its attention to those turning out boats in significant quantities, and few dinghies are examined. Most dinghy builders, however, seem to have made the effort to comply.

When the regulations noted that foam flotation had to be protected from shrinkage and damage caused by exposure to gasoline or other materials, those who had been installing raw blocks of foam beneath thwarts either enclosed the foam or began using a more resistant material. A number of dinghy builders go out of their way to demonstrate the flotation qualities of their boats, a point that buyers should keep in mind. If a boat in which you are interested does not carry a yellow-and-black certification label, *ask why,* and go to whatever lengths are necessary to determine whether or not the level-flotation guidelines are met.

Level Flotation and "Traditional" Small Craft

At the time the level-flotation requirement was first enacted, there was criticism from some builders and enthusiasts of traditional-style boats who noted that the rules seemed geared for mass manufacturers. "It didn't seem fair," said one, "that a traditional pulling boat or dory had to meet the same requirements as a fiberglass speedboat. There was no way to do it without messing up the boat's looks with strips of foam."

In fact, during 1975, the Coast Guard spent more than 150 man-hours testing four traditional boats. These were a 14-foot 10-inch fisherman's dory, an 11-foot 9-inch Swampscott dory skiff (both built by the Strawberry Banke boatshop in Portsmouth, New Hampshire), a 14-foot peapod supplied by Mystic Seaport's John Gardner, and a 12-foot Old Town skiff of 1950s vintage. These boats were built according to traditional scantlings (the dimensions of the boat's frames and planks) and carried no foam.

Each of them passed the flotation guidelines proposed for manually propelled craft, suggesting to the test team that "these traditional boats (and especially those intended for manual propulsion) should be exempt from any level-flotation requirement." The report also noted that the addition of flotation along the gunwales of such boats would "necessitate a drastic change in the construction of the boats and detract from their traditional appearance and aesthetic appeal."

When the flotation requirements passed into law, however, wooden boats had to meet them, although a Coast Guard Boating Safety circular did note that dinghies, yacht tenders, and traditional craft built of wood could "in most instances . . . satisfy the requirements without additional flotation." The reference here was to boats rated for less than 2 hp or for no power at all, but the decision led to controversy that continues today, although it perhaps has grown less heated. "Because we didn't say things like, 'Dories are the safest boats ever made,'" said a Coast Guard officer familiar with the problem, "the rules became an emotional issue with some people."

A lot of traditional small-boat enthusiasts seemed to think people only became statistics in fiberglass or aluminum runabouts. But although many traditional boat designs have proven themselves seaworthy—usually in the hands of experienced, sometimes professional, seamen—there are situations that will swamp or capsize them. In that case, level flotation will help the man in the dory as much as it will help the man in the speedboat. Coast Guard tests suggest, too, that wooden small craft built to lighter-than-traditional scantlings—whether to save weight or to save cost—might well need foam to meet the requirements.

Today, most of the criticism has been stilled, and even those who were staunch opponents of rules now 10 years old have found them to be workable. Most builders of traditional wooden dinghies do not certify them to carry an outboard. Thus, the boats must comply with the less-demanding 2/15 requirement, which some refer to as "the dinghy rule."

Lowell's Boat Shop, among the relatively few shops turning out wooden small craft on a more or less production basis, is among the firms that have taken this approach and followed the 2/15 rule. The shop's larger boats, however, are certified for engines of more than 2 hp and do meet level-flotation guidelines. "We have tested the boats," said Lowell's Jim Odell, "and we saw that level flotation works. It adds to the price, but it works. The chief problem in larger wooden boats, with the foam up the sides, is to avoid dry rot caused by condensation. So far, the best method we've found is to epoxy the planking behind the foam."

Concerned as it must be with the safety of the boating public, the Coast Guard takes a realistic approach to wooden dinghies and small craft of traditional design and build. "Our reasoning," said one officer, "is that if a shop builds a boat or two a year, the impact on public safety is not large. But if a manufacturer builds a thousand boats a year, the impact can be large, indeed." The Coast Guard is also flexible enough to authorize brass as yellow enough for the builder who finds the required bright yellow certification label too garish for his boat.

Whatever you may think about Coast Guard flotation requirements, don't rely on them alone. Buy or make from a plastic jug a bailer, and keep it lashed to the boat. Although Coast Guard regulations require that you have flotation devices aboard, remember that *wearing* a life vest is anything but a dumb idea, especially if conditions are poor.

Towing a Tender

Unless one buys or builds the very smallest of tenders, or is willing to deflate and has room to stow an inflatable, towing will be necessary when cruising. Even yachts of 30 or 35 feet may barely have deck or cabintop space for an 8-footer. Those that do may require a dinghy with an excessively low sheer to clear the boom, compromising the dinghy's carrying ability and performance. What's worse, such dinghies may be hoisted aboard infrequently, thus minimizing their one real advantage. You may be better off if you buy a larger dinghy of good design and tow it.

If there is an advantage to towing a dinghy, it is that the tender can be larger and more able. Despite this, many sailors choose the tiniest cockleshell possible, believing that small size alone will reduce drag to a minimum. Yet, as noted in chapter 2, a well-designed dinghy of 9 to 12 feet in length can produce less drag when towing than a smaller boat. This invariably comes as a surprise to those who have sold an 8-footer and bought a 12-foot dinghy.

Furthermore, the size of the boat doing the towing need not dictate the size of the dinghy. A small cruiser may well be better off seeking the best towing boat rather than the tiniest dinghy. The question of towing various-sized dinghies reaches extremes, indicating that state of mind and personal insecurities may play an important role. One skipper disdained to tow a 7 1/2-foot dinghy behind his highly instrumented Pearson 365 because he "could always feel it holding us back." He bought an inflatable, which he then complained took too much time to pump up. Another sailor, the owner of an 18-foot catboat who regularly tows an 8-foot dinghy, is never bothered by its presence. Yet, another, an owner of a 33-foot sloop, reported that towing a 13 1/2-foot Whitehall-style dinghy produced less drag than his previous small pram, which, "at 6 knots would rear back and pull like an elephant."

There are those who reject towing a large dinghy not only because they believe it will slow them more than a smaller dinghy would, but also because it would "look funny." This is a subjective matter, conditioned by what people these days are accustomed to. Yachting photographs taken 50 to 100 years ago commonly show boats trailing dinghies nearly half their size.

Because every dinghy tows differently, the best location for the bow eye depends to a large degree on the particular boat involved. Generally, a towing eye located low on the stem is preferable. As mentioned in chapter 2, prams, in particular, need the eye installed low to lift the bow transom slightly and keep it from shoveling up water. On stem-type (pointy-bow) dinghies, the bow eye generally will be found partway up the stem, allowing the dinghy to ride at its normal waterline while being towed.

Some of the larger round-bottomed dinghies, which ride buoyantly on the quarter wave of the larger vessel, tow perfectly well from a point on the breasthook. Designer/builder Jarvis Newman noted that his 12-footer doesn't need "a big blob of a tow eye on it. Whether it's towed at 5, 10, or 20 knots, the boat has a tendency to pull up, and the breasthook-mounted painter pulls it down just enough. The tendency otherwise would be for the stern (which is quite fine-lined) to go down quite a ways. As it is, the boat tows with little drag. You can hold it with one finger at 6 knots."

Doing away with an external bow eye also eliminates the opportunity for it to damage the yacht's transom—often a problem unless the eye is located well down on a sharply raked stem. Do not underestimate the potential problems a protruding bow eye can create. The possibility of damage is present when coming alongside, when using the dinghy as a work platform and when towing. Some builders minimize this hazard by using a towing *ring* that can pivot down when not in use.

Towing an inflatable poses problems of its own. Most such boats are best towed close to the transom; otherwise, they are liable to flip over—the major reason for removing the oars, motor, and any loose gear. Indeed, it is common practice on large boats with unobstructed afterdecks to pull the bow of an inflatable up and over the transom for towing. While an inflatable usually can be towed safely from its painter, it is best to use a bridle attached to a pair of stainless rings for heavy-duty towing. If it appears that the bridle will chafe the buoyancy tubes, soft plastic tubing or some other antichafe gear should be used.

The Towline (Painter)

Only two things stand between you and a lost dinghy: a sturdy bow eye (rarely but *occasionally* a problem) and the painter. Just as you must watch for chafe on a halyard or sheet, so must you protect and inspect the painter. Three-eighths or 1/2-inch three-strand nylon makes a good, elastic towline, and I've seen dinghies towed for years of fair weather on 3/16-inch line. Dacron line can be used to make up a painter, too, but it is then a good idea to include a rubber snubber to act as a shock absorber.

Three-strand, 3/8-inch line has a tensile strength of some 3,700 pounds. Braided line is 30 percent stronger, but you may require the services of a professional to make the necessary eyesplice in one end. Polypropylene is favored by some as a dinghy painter. Its chief virtue is that it floats and thus is unlikely ever to foul the propeller. Its tensile strength, however, is less than that of nylon or dacron, so it needs to be twice the diameter. Nor does it take knots well, and belaying it securely can be a "slippery" business. As noted in chapter 5 polypropylene is subject to ultraviolet breakdown, and you need to check it regularly. Once it has begun to fade seriously, view it with suspicion.

Towlines should be at least 25 feet long, but heavy-duty towing demands a line up to 75 feet in length. The longer line will allow the dinghy to ride well astern in following seas, or at higher speeds in order to get the dinghy completely clear of the boat's wake. People have towed dinghies like this for a lifetime of summer cruising, adjusting the painter so that both yacht and

A good painter. A thimble and eyesplice in three-strand nylon line provide a stretchy towline that won't chafe at the bow eye.

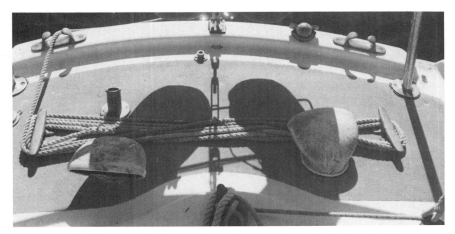

This 3/8-inch, 75-foot nylon painter is neatly secured to cleats aboard a Pearson Triton. It is easily adjusted and the fairlead protects it from chafe.

dinghy ascend and descend waves in unison. Should the dinghy threaten to outpace the larger boat, a bight of line, or a small bucket, can be towed. Treat the use of any such retarding device as you would tucking in a reef: Have the line rigged and overboard before you need it. For convenience, any dinghy equipped with a long towline or lines should have a shorter painter for everyday use.

Note that, for serious towing, it is desirable to have two painters (one with some slack in it) attached to *different* points on the dinghy. That will help protect against a boat's being lost because of a broken painter or a bow eye that shatters under extreme loads. It also permits the second line to be cast off to act as a drag, should that be necessary.

An English Sailor Writes About Using Two Painters

British author and designer Maurice Griffiths shackled *both* painters to his dinghy's stem fitting. When seas steepened, "We now cast off one of these to trail astern as a drogue, and veered the stouter one to about six fathoms. This arrangement, we had found, was more effective in braking the dinghy's wild rush down the face of a following sea, as it allowed its stern to slew to one side or the other if it wanted to. If the drogueline is towed from the stern it is less effective, as it keeps the dinghy's transom square on to the seas. Moreover, when no longer running before it, it is much easier to retrieve the drogue painter from the dinghy's stem than from its transom, while the yacht is still traveling at all fast."

—Maurice Griffiths, *The First of the Tide*

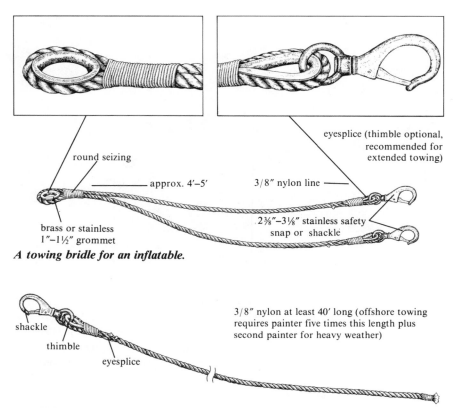

A towing bridle for an inflatable.

Dinghy painter.

At the bow eye, the painter should be fitted with a thimble and eyesplice. An alternative is an *oversized* snapshackle.

Towing Considerations

There are no secrets to successful towing other than practice, *observation,* and experimentation. Do provide the best fairlead possible for the painter and watch for chafe, but don't always watch the other guy. You'll occasionally see a lobsterman towing his dinghy right at his transom—at 18 knots! Remember to haul the dinghy in close when you are docking or maneuvering under power to reduce the chance of snagging the painter with your propeller. Attaching a few floats to the painter can also help in this regard.

No matter how well a dinghy may tow during even rough conditions, once it begins taking on wind-blown spray in quantity, its performance will deteriorate quickly as the water sloshes back and forth, increasing weight

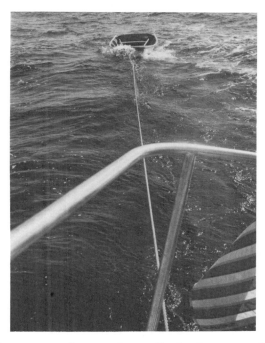

A pram shovels up some salt water. Even a dinghy that tows well will take on some water—a warning that towing gear must be in excellent shape. A second line for safety's sake can be useful in really rough weather. A bailer and sponge secured aboard will speed drying out the boat when you make harbor.

When maneuvering, keep the dinghy close astern so the painter will stay clear of your propeller.

and—because the boat is pressed lower in the water—drag. But it's difficult to stop to bail out a dinghy in rough conditions.

Relatively few production dinghies are equipped with self-bailers. Those that are have bailing arrangements intended mainly for keeping the bottom dry during rain showers or on a row to the mooring. For serious offshore work, you will probably have to devise your own self-bailer if you want one. A practical arrangement is likely to be difficult or expensive on most production boats. If a tender does not have a hollow skeg, for instance, fitting a rubber valve-type bailer will be out of the question unless you bore a long hole. Fitting the bailer to the hole in a permanent, watertight manner is seldom simple, either, as cracked layers of putty sometimes attest. Installing a transom-mounted bailer may be even more impractical, because the transom is so often the backing point for a foam-filled seat. In that case, some system of pipes would have to be installed through the foam.

In most dinghies, the only alternative is a semi-automatic bailer installed at a low point in the hull. A scupper-type arrangement is most practical in a wooden or fiberglass dinghy with longitudinal flotation that leaves the transom comparatively accessible. Chances are that anyone who sails in conditions where a really efficient bailer would be helpful will have the dinghy stowed securely on deck.

On the subject of water in dinghies, two other aspects deserve mention—the center thwart and the daggerboard trunk. Boats in which the center thwart rests atop a foam-filled bulkhead need a good-sized limber hole through the structure, permitting easy passage of water forward and aft. The daggerboard trunk itself may be a possible source of water, especially when towing at higher speeds, which create substantial pressure within the trunk. A tight-fitting plug should extend down to the keel to reduce turbulence. Some mechanical provision for holding the plug in place, with shockcord or lashing, is very much in order for a daggerboard-equipped sailing dinghy that will be towed regularly.

Making Things Secure

"After attaching the tow tope, he coiled down the painter in the bow of the pram, put the sponge in the dory bailer, and jammed the bailer in a certain place under the forward thwart. He next took the oars and, one after the other, tucked their handles or grips under the forward thwart and slid them forward enough so the blade could be sprung down under the after thwart. He then slid the oars outboard as far as they would go so that if one were to board the dinghy hurriedly in a seaway the oars would be out of the way. Goddard next jammed the oarlocks between the planking and seat strings and said to himself: 'I guess nothing will get loose or bang now even if we slam into a head sea all day.'"

—L. Francis Herreshoff, *The Compleat Cruiser*

While securing things is often practical, I'd think twice before making a long passage with *any* gear aboard the dinghy, or with the outboard still on the transom. If you do leave the outboard mounted for a short haul in calm weather, be sure to raise it to minimize drag. When towing my own inflatable, or even leaving it at the mooring, I remove everything including the oars. It's one pretty sure method to avoid loss!

Stowing

During the early years of this century, a *Rudder* magazine contributor named Winfield Thompson described the design of a tender for his Crosby catboat. He sized the dinghy so it would just fit inside the cockpit coamings and across the boat. The Wee Pup pram was 7 feet 6 inches overall and, when stowed, still left room for handling sheet and wheel. In an age when tenders usually were larger, the Wee Pup charmed all who saw it. Thompson had gotten what he wanted—a dinghy that could be brought aboard if he wished.

Stowing a dinghy in the cockpit is not an ideal arrangement, of course, and few boats have cockpits approaching the dimensions of Thompson's 25-foot catboat. Most sailors who keep a dinghy on board must find room for it

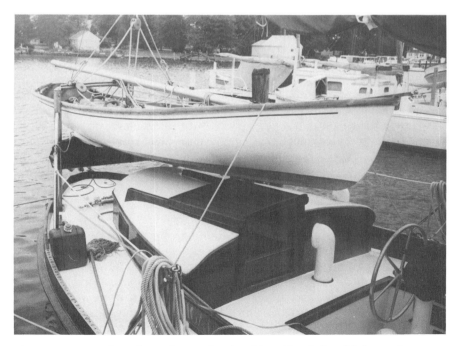

This Newman tender is hoisted atop the aft cabin with a halyard led to a sheet winch. It sits in a special cradle with its spars stowed inside the hull.

elsewhere, on cabintop or deck, not an easy thing on many boats. Few designers these days give much thought to dinghy stowage, and the change from CCA to IOR rules also affected the situation, because the mast position was farther aft, and appropriate space for a dinghy was lost. Center-cockpit boats seem little better. Only a few cruising boats have cabintop dinghy stowage as an integral part of their design.

The problem is less acute aboard powerboats intended for cruising. Many trawler yachts have both deck space and lifting booms easily able to accommodate a dinghy. Powerboats with wide transom sterns are also well suited to carrying the dinghy in davits, an arrangement that makes literal child's play of launching and hoisting. Davits may present problems on a sailboat, however. Aside from questions of aesthetics, the devices add some 5 feet to a vessel's length, and a yacht needs adequate displacement aft to carry the increased load.

Davit manufacturers like to stress the safety aspects of their products, noting that a dinghy on davits can be launched quickly in case of fire or other emergency. The point is well made, as few sailboats with dinghies on deck have gear for quick launching. Any dinghy on davits, however, whether rigid or inflatable, should be secured well to keep it from swinging and to guard against chafe. The dinghy should also be fitted with a bilge drain (which can be removed when the boat puts to sea) or a tight-fitting cover. While it may be unlikely that the average coastwise cruiser will be caught out in seas big enough to swamp a dinghy on davits, the possibility exists, and the prospect of carrying a vastly heavy dinghy out beyond your stern is not pleasant.

Many cruising sailors prefer stowing to towing, and they find a way to lift the dinghy aboard either by brute strength or with the aid of a halyard. Tiny prams such as the Bill Peterson boat discussed in chapter 2 are ideal for bringing aboard without mechanical aids. But the topsides and toerail need to be protected by a heavy piece of canvas or some other means. The alternative is to use a halyard or topping lift attached to a bridle to bring the dinghy aboard. While this is often a two-person job—one working the lifting tackle, the other guiding the boat—it can be done alone. I met one 73-year-old singlehander who regularly launches his 12-foot tender using a tackle rigged to the boom and a sheet winch.

On larger yachts, it is often practical to stow the dinghy right-side-up on deck, thus allowing the spars, oars, and perhaps a jerry jug or two to be carried conveniently. A tight-fitting cover will keep out water (and slowly accumulating junk), especially in heavy weather. On smaller boats with comparatively low freeboard, it is best to stow the dinghy inverted, reducing windage and presenting a stout bottom to the impact of boarding seas. Generally, it is most convenient to carry a dinghy atop the cabin. If space abaft the mast is inadequate, the foredeck is about the only alternative. Most find this location

Tied down by canvas straps through stout eyebolts, this Dyer dinghy, with its modest freeboard, fits neatly out of the way beneath the boom.

a poor compromise. The dinghy then often covers the forward hatch, obstructing ventilation and sailhandling. Unless the yacht has been laid out with foredeck dinghy stowage in mind, it's also likely to get in the way of various sheets and fittings.

Wherever stowed, the dinghy must be tied down securely. Use polyester lines or canvas straps attached to eyebolts in the deck or cabin roof. Bill Peterson designed a toggle that goes from a deck-mounted eyebolt up through his pram's oarlock sockets, which are mounted solidly to the rugged gunwale (another reason to reinforce a dinghy's flanged fiberglass gunwale). Dinghies pulled up on floats or docks should also be well secured. A posh prep school once lost its entire dinghy fleet to a sudden storm: Not one of the boats had been tied down.

Rowing

No matter what its size or type, a dinghy's performance can be improved if you give some attention to rowing technique. This is true whether the boat is a tiny pram or a comparatively lean 12-footer. In the case of the pram, for example, consider that the oar blades, if not feathered, may actually rival the bow transom in size. That means extra wind resistance.

Properly rowed, a well-designed dinghy, particularly a larger model, can perform impressively—so impressively that it may outperform a smaller boat equipped with an outboard. It may also require fewer trips because of its increased load capacity.

The accompanying sketch by Newport designer Eric Sponberg suggests an efficient rowing motion. It shows oars long enough, and a gunwale high enough (see Chapter 2 for further discussion of these dimensions) to permit the hands to travel back and forth about 6 to 9 inches above the knees and thighs. The sketch shows overlapping oars—one hand placed in front of the other on the boat's centerline, maximizing leverage. The alternative, hands placed in front of the shoulder, is not as effective because leverage is reduced and added work is required. Dropping the wrists at the end of each stroke will "feather" the oars, bringing the blades parallel with the water's surface and reducing windage. Note that installing a foot brace or "stretcher" will significantly add to the power you can develop when pulling the oars.

Most dinghies seem happiest with a moderate stroke. Reaching back in an exaggerated fashion accomplishes little and will soon wear you out. More often, particularly in small boats, a quicker, shorter stroke will be necessary to keep the boat moving, especially across a current or wind. Always aim well upwind or upcurrent of your destination. This gives you a bit of breathing time toward the end of your row when you are approaching the boat or shore and perhaps have less energy to expend than when you shoved off.

Those accustomed to shorter dinghies should keep in mind—when first rowing a larger one—that the bigger boat will be rather less maneuverable and tend to *carry much farther* between strokes. You need to plan ahead when approaching the boat or dock, begin your turn earlier, and plan to remove the oars and locks in plenty of time to avoid damaging either them or the boat's topsides. Practice coming alongside gently and using the offside oar to keep the dinghy alongside while you hold on to the boat or dock with your other hand. Although few boats can be rowed comfortably while facing forward, doing so is worth a try, especially if you routinely have to thread your way through a crowded anchorage.

Bottom Paint and a Bailer

Once you have become a proficient oarsman, you can get the most from a tender, using it to work out muscle cramps and a stiff back after a day at the helm. While rowing, you can give some thought to applying bottom paint to the dinghy, for if it spends most of its time in the water, bottom paint will be necessary. Think about a boottop stripe, too. Nothing makes a dinghy look more like a *yacht* tender than a neat stripe at the waterline, contrasting with a

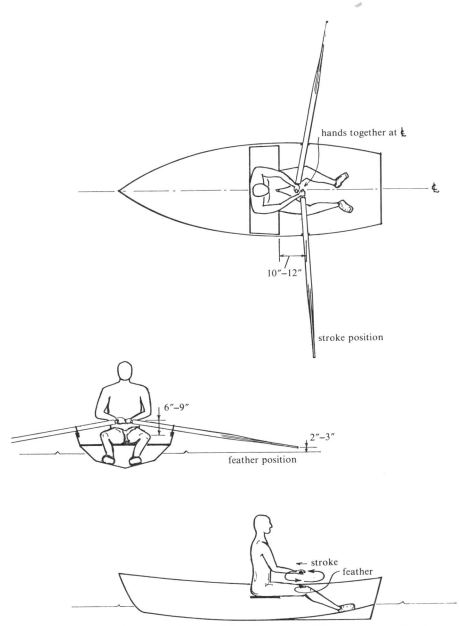

Eric Sponberg drew these thought-provoking diagrams to illustrate some effective dimensions and techniques. The rower here has his overlapped hands on the centerline, the most effective position.

Wrists raised for pulling (left) . . . dropped for feathering (right).

Bracing one's feet against a foot brace or stretcher mounted about 2 feet from the rowing thwart can appreciably increase one's rowing power. It is especially useful in rough conditions. Sometimes, feet can be braced against the frame of a wood boat. A stretcher should be as unobtrusive as possible.

glossy hull and nicely kept woodwork. In the interest of neatness, keep a boat bailer attached to a thwart or fitting, and a sponge or old towel aboard to mop up with.

The Dinghy as Towboat

In addition to its other uses, a dinghy can also serve as auxiliary power to move your larger boat, should the latter's power fail. This *can* be done under oarpower, using steady strokes and a long line to avoid jerks. Boats have been towed surprisingly long distances by one or two rowers in calm weather.

Pulling and feathering. The three photos illustrate a good stroke.

Attempting to tow a boat with an outboard-powered dinghy is risky, because the towline could foul the propeller or even capsize the dinghy if the pull came from any direction but dead astern. A bridle arrangement can be developed to skirt this problem, but lashing the dinghy alongside against fenders with a bow, stern, and spring line can be quite effective. In calm or light winds, a dinghy equipped with a slow-turning outboard of even 2 hp can move a surprisingly heavy boat. A 4 hp motor would be better yet.

Rowing Out an Anchor

The dinghy can also be used to row out an anchor in rough weather or after a grounding, potentially one of the most important maneuvers it will be called upon to perform. But this is the very act that nearly drowned Joshua Slocum, as competent a seaman as ever sailed, so caution is necessary. The most obvious danger is capsizing the dinghy while handling the anchor and/or becoming entangled in the anchor rode. You can often hook an anchor over the transom, or in a sculling notch if one is present.

Arrange the anchor chain carefully in the dinghy. If the line itself is to be carried in the dinghy rather than paid out from the yacht itself, it needs to be coiled very carefully and its end well secured to a thwart or cleat. A particularly heavy anchor ideally would be secured with a quick-release knot (perhaps tied to the center thwart), toggle, or line that could be cut with a knife when the appropriate spot is reached.

The only time I ever witnessed a boat aground that desperately needed to have an anchor rowed out to windward, the inexperienced skipper and crew had no concept of the maneuver, and their swimming pool–type inflatable with its tiny oars had no hope of carrying the anchor anywhere. The boat was eventually towed off the beach with unknown damage to its fin keel. Cruisers should practice carrying out an anchor in reasonably calm weather to familiarize themselves with the possible pitfalls involved.

A Dinghy's Anchor

A small anchor for use only with the dinghy is a useful bit of gear. With it, you can beach the boat at low tide and not worry that the dinghy might float off while you're ashore exploring. An anchor can be handy for an occasional fishing trip, and someday, perhaps, might save you from being carried in a direction precisely opposite to that in which you wish to go. A variety of small folding grapnel, mushroom, or Danforth anchors is available. Bending the dinghy anchor to its own rode, rather than a towing painter, is preferable. That way, a chafed anchor rode won't be called upon for towing duty. Keep the anchor line coiled neatly and seized with some easily cut lashings, or in a bucket or canvas bag. Otherwise, you'll always have a frustrating mess underfoot.

Securing an anchor rode, or any other line, to a dinghy can be rather discouraging. There usually isn't much in the way of extra fittings. Unfortunately, you're not likely to notice this troublesome shortcoming until it's too late and you are struggling to tie a dinghy alongside, by both bow and stern, or lash it atop an automobile roofrack. Sailing models have some advantage here, since at least it is possible to feed a line through the rudder fittings.

Adding cleats to a fiberglass dinghy is likely to be difficult. The installation will invariably require planning and, quite possibly, the addition of stern knees and a breasthook. Some owners, in desperation, bore holes right through the gunwale to take a line. As always, it is easier to make additions to a wooden boat than to a fiberglass model. If you just need a place to secure a line aft, U-shaped grab handles, through-bolted on either side of the transom may well suffice. They'll also facilitate lifting and carrying the boat.

Note that an anchor can be a potentially important piece of safety gear for your dinghy, just as for your larger boat. This is particularly true for inflatables. One reads of people blown out to sea and lost when they could not row their inflatable dinghies against a high wind. This is something to keep in mind *whenever* using an inflatable in an exposed harbor.

Lifting and Carrying

The business of moving your dinghy requires careful thought. An 85- to 100-pound dinghy, while not that heavy in itself, is an *awkward* object on land, and it can strain the physical resources of two fit men. No matter where you take hold, you find yourself taking shortened crablike steps, your wrists bent at odd angles. If you're at the bow, you usually think you have the worst end of the deal—until you try the stern. Carrying the boat by the gunwale works reasonably well. Some dinghies have handholds cut out of the middle thwart, which helps matters, but this can only be accomplished on tenders without foam-filled middle bulkheads.

A boat with a wooden breasthook can sometimes be handled ashore rather easily if the bottom of the breasthook is hollowed slightly to let fingers get a grip. (See the photograph in "The Bow Eye" section of Chapter 3.) This extra bit of craftsmanship makes it surprisingly easy to pull even a quite heavy dinghy onto a beach or float. It can also help when carrying a dinghy. Smaller tenders, 8-footers and less, can sometimes be hefted by slipping an arm under the middle thwart and lifting the boat on one's shoulder or back. Those who regularly take their dinghies home, or who must carry the boat some distance to the water, should investigate the various dinghy carriers and dollies available. Transom-mounted wheels (such as those pictured in Chapter 1), or ones that mount in the daggerboard slot, have much to recommend them. So does a simple wooden roller (one can be cut from a broomstick), especially if you only need to maneuver your dinghy from float rack to water.

While carrying a dinghy home involves some drudgery at the end of each sail, it is the best way to keep a boat from being damaged or stolen. Some people, in fact, expressly choose boats small enough to fit right inside a station wagon.

Whether you take your dinghy home, leave it aboard, or stow it in a dinghy rack, take the time to make it distinctive. Paint your boat's name on it. Carve its serial number or some other identification in an easily visible place. Then mark it a second time in some not-so-apparent location. There's something to be said for adding your phone number and address, too. If the dinghy ever does break loose from a towline, some honest soul might find it and call you. Finally, lock the dinghy with a chain and a rust-resistant lock. If you don't want to take the oars with you, invest in one of those devices designed to secure them to the boat, or drill a hole through the blades to accept the chain.

Think Safety!

As harbors fill to capacity, with boats moored even in areas of marginal protection, the importance of safe dinghy handling needs to be kept always in mind. If you have guests aboard, you'll have to instill safety in their minds, too. That process begins even before anyone steps into the boat. It's amazing how many people, even sober ones, overlook the common sense way of boarding a small boat: step into its center, don't step on its gunwale or thwart. Likewise, once seated, remain seated until you've reached your destination.

If you will be motoring, remember that most dinghies are cramped: beware the elbow pulling the starter cord. In fact, if your dinghy's outboard is equipped with a neutral, it's best to start the engine, let it warm up, and briefly engage forward as a trial before boarding passengers. Distribute weight evenly. Underway, do things smoothly, whether speeding up, slowing down, or turning. Keep a lookout. There's plenty to hit in a harbor, and plenty of other dinghies scooting about, too.

If you will be taking off from, or landing on, a beach, never discount the force of even a modest swell. Coming in, keep the stern to the waves, time your landing, and raise the outboard before the propeller hits bottom. Heading out, keep the bow pointed into the swell. It is surprising how wet things will get if you don't.

Here are some more basic tips:

Oars.   Don't trust the motor alone; always have oars *and* oarlocks. Don't assume you'll be able to use oars as paddles and make headway against a strong wind or tide.

Bailers.   Rigid dinghies should have bailers *secured* to the boat at all times on a long lanyard.

Painter.   The dinghy painter should be in good condition, and well up to securing you to a mooring or boat, should that be necessary for any reason.

Lifeline.   The hull of an overturned dinghy can be a distressingly difficult and featureless surface for a cold and frightened capsize victim to grasp. While inflatables routinely have lifelines along their sides, rigid dinghies do not, and thus lack a good handhold. Bottom strakes that can double as handholds, a sturdy lifeline with flotation buoys, or both, make good sense.

Color. Although some dinghies are molded or painted in a dark color to match the larger boat, the added visibility offered by a white dinghy may someday prove to be important.

Inflatables. Remember that the drift of an inflatable can be slowed if the boat is swamped, and check polypropylene lifelines regularly, especially if the boat is left inflated and exposed to sunlight. Such line will eventually rot and turn to powder when subjected to a *pull*.

Gear. Carry a knife. You simply never know when it may come in handy, either to help yourself or someone else. A personal flotation device, in addition to being a Coast Guard requirement, is a good idea, even though your dinghy can float when swamped. All Type I, II, and III vests are designed to keep the wearer afloat with his face out of the water, but Type I PFDs do this best. Cold water will be quickly debilitating. A hand-held VHF radio, some signaling devices, or both could come in handy should you ever find yourself being carried out to sea.

Summary

- Towing painters should be a *minimum* 5/16-inch to 3/8-inch-diameter nylon and at least 20 feet long (double that or more for frequent, coastwise cruising), to give maximum flexibility under varying conditions.

- Serious towing requires a sturdy bow eye, preferably one backed by a solid hardwood block. (Even 2-inch washers used as backing have been known to pull right through a dinghy's stem.)

- Practice rowing and feathering the oars.

- Don't take any dinghy for granted. Step into it carefully, remembering that very light boats will be skittish.

- Don't take landing at or launching from a beach for granted. Keep your bow or stern square to any swell; even modest waves are powerful.

- Whatever your boat's rated weight capacity, reduce it in rough conditions. It's better to make two trips dry than one that results in getting wet, or worse.

- Always think safety—for you and your passengers. Watch out for the other guy, and carry PFDs.

- Enjoy!

CHAPTER SEVEN

Builders and Boats

*W*HO builds small craft these days, and what sorts of boats are they turning out? This chapter provides an overview of the kind of company and individual involved in the dinghy business, and it also serves as a descriptive catalog of what's available.

THE building of small boats is worlds removed from corporate life, the nine-to-five job, or even the building and selling of larger sail- or powerboats. It is not an easy calling. Most small-boat builders must struggle to earn a living, and most do so in locations where the cost of living is comparatively moderate. Overheads need to be kept rigorously low; hours are long, and the builder who doesn't do almost everything himself—as opposed to subcontracting—is unlikely to succeed. Within the space of time during which this book was written and produced, several dinghy builders closed their doors. Another put his molds in mothballs, frustrated by indifferent suppliers and tight profit margins.

In fact, if a small-boat builder is not independently wealthy, or a retiree keeping busy, he is embarked upon a difficult road, indeed. Often enough, the road leads to bigger boats or some related work, and the building and selling of dinghies becomes a sideline or is set aside, the molds sold to another would-be dinghy builder. Nevertheless, the lure of "owning one's own business," and the notion of earning a living by working in a field one truly enjoys, exerts an irresistible attraction. I don't know what the statistics are—or even whether any exist—but the rate of dinghy business closings and start-ups must be reasonably high. Somewhere, someplace, somebody is starting out with high hopes, while elsewhere, somebody is offering a set of molds for sale as a turnkey operation.

Like the world of larger boats, sailboats in particular, the dinghy market is both finite in size and hugely fragmented. There are any number of builders, all

The low cost of some dinghies is made possible, in part, by mass-production methods.

hoping to sell boats to roughly the same market. And the price of those boats, even if they may seem high to buyers, is not enough to live on without a substantial sales volume. If you consider that a 20 percent margin on a $1,000 boat may not cover overhead and marketing expenses, you have an idea of what the dinghy builder is up against. For this reason, dinghy building is a labor of love for many boatbuilders.

Although real success as a small-boat builder means attaining some measure of volume, that volume is often difficult to achieve. Only by establishing a dealer network can volume production—and its efficiencies—be gained; but few chandleries need to add yet another dinghy to their inventory. Most already handle more than one. Dealerships that sell larger boats are likely outlets, but it doesn't take much imagination to perceive that a boat salesman, like a boatbuilder, makes a lot more money by selling one big boat than lots of dinghies. Guess where the major efforts are expended!

Distribution, then, is a significant problem for the great majority of dinghy builders. Few have achieved the success of Eli Jehassi, an Israeli immigrant who arrived in the United States in 1968. After working for a dinghy producer on Long Island, building molds for other boatbuilders and a variety of other fiberglass components, Eli began building a dinghy of his own at home in his garage. In his battered red Dodge, he took these boats to every boat dealership he could reach on a weekend. The inexpensive yet well-finished dinghies were successful sellers, permitting Jehassi to expand production to a variety of models.

Within a decade, Eli became perhaps the largest volume producer of fiberglass dinghies anywhere. With pricing, product, and timing in his favor, he carved a substantial niche for his company in a market segment that offers a purely dinghy-making company the greatest potential for success: volume-produced, low-priced boats. Today, several companies produce similarly priced boats in volume, and I no longer know who can claim to be the biggest seller.

Few manufacturers or would-be manufacturers have been as skilled or fortunate as those who manage to produce several hundred or more dinghies per year. One hopeful ceased his efforts eight months after operations began, with a single boat to show for his efforts but not a single dealer. Like many others, that builder had planned to produce a "Dyer-quality" dinghy at a lower price and market it through dealers. But the dealers already had Dyers at the high end and Elis or another model at the low-to-medium end, and they were not interested. This particular builder had enough business experience to have a business plan, and once he recognized he could never achieve the dealer network necessary to his required volume, he ceased operations and kept his losses to a minimum. He also took away with him one *very* interesting yacht tender that would never see production.

Rather than merchandising through a dealer network, most dinghy builders are left to their own devices, selling their boats locally or regionally through word of mouth, long rounds of boat-show appearances, and ads in the more affordable magazines. Most have a brochure of some sort, even if only a sheet of paper printed on one side. Regrettably, few of these documents explain in a meaningful way the goals of the boat's designer, or its unique construction and performance features.

Overall, the business does not appear to be susceptible to sophisticated marketing techniques, but advertising budgets would be quite limited even if it were. Furthermore, the great majority of small-boat builders are craftsmen first and foremost, and they would claim to have little marketing savvy. Those whose businesses survive to prosper in any way achieve this only through intense dedication and an understanding of the limited financial rewards to be reaped by a "dinghy-only" business. That is why dinghies are a sideline for so many. Dyer, to cite but one example, sells a line of highly regarded powerboats. Builders of wooden dinghies almost invariably restore or build larger wooden boats. Successful volume builders of fiberglass dinghies often offer a full line of small craft from 7 to 12 or 13 feet in length.

Occasionally, of course, one discovers dinghy builders who have no particularly ambitious plans for their companies. Instead of going to boat shows and distributing brochures, they stay in the shop, relying on word-of-mouth advertising and a small ad here and there. Such attitudes, which would be inexplicable in the "normal" business world, are not at all unusual among dinghy builders. Some have been in business for a decade or more and remain unknown to potential buyers 100 miles away.

What does all this have to do with you, the would-be dinghy purchaser? It is merely background about those with whom you may be doing business. Often enough, you may be dealing with the builder himself. When a price is quoted, it helps to know where the builder is coming from. His margin is probably thin, and his room for negotiation limited.

When you buy a dinghy, chances are you will do so from a chandlery, a boat dealership, or the builder himself. By and large, the market decides what dinghies are worth, and within a given price range, markups are seldom unreasonable. The best prices tend to be "show specials," but there is not so much money to be made from building and selling small boats that anyone can expect to get "a steal." Bargains do appear, of course, but you have to know what you want and be in the right place at the right time to take advantage of them.

The price of most professionally built wooden dinghies has long since surpassed the means of the average person, and such boats have unfortunately entered into the realm of playthings for the wealthy. Yet the price of such well-built craft is reasonable given the hours involved in their construction, the cost of materials, and the overhead even a modest shop faces. At times, one wonders how the price is kept so *low*.

Notes on the Catalog

The following catalog of boats is as comprehensive as possible. I am not aware of *every* boat being built or every kit or plans set available. Nor did all the companies contacted respond to my questionnaire. Not surprisingly, several builders who appeared in the first edition of this book are no longer in business. The listing includes both rigid and inflatable dinghies. In the latter case, only manufacturers catering to the U.S. yacht-tender market have been included. Prices and specifications were as accurate as possible at the time of publication.

The comments accompanying the boats are based on personal observation, reports from owners, and, occasionally, the builder's thoughts and remarks. It is my personal impression that the fiberglass work of the majority of low-to-moderate-priced dinghies is acceptable and comparable. The chief items that distinguish the boats are: design, rubrails, freeboard, thwart attachments and the relationship of the thwart to the oarlock sockets, and hardware and its mounting. In many, but certainly not all, cases, such features also are comparable, but *take nothing for granted.* Don't be afraid to measure, inspect, and compare. And remember that even a very fine boat may still require a custom touch or two—a cleat here, a lifting handle there, a foot brace, a rubbing strake—to adapt it to meet all your needs.

A Dinghy Rating Checklist

The following checklist will help you make a quick assessment of any dinghy in which you are interested. The greater the number of "yes" answers, the better the boat. Remember that it is *always* best to try a boat—to row it alone and also with another person aboard. If you plan to invest in a sailing dinghy, be *sure* to try it first under both oars and rig.

Construction Considerations

- Wooden gunwale?   yes   no
- Wood/metal-backed towing eye?   yes   no
- Center support for middle thwart?   yes   no
- Is there some "crush space" between the hull and the end of the thwart?   yes   no
- Bronze/stainless hardware?   yes   no
- Wooden stern knees reinforcing transom?   yes   no
- Bow seat located for rowing/two sets of oarlock sockets?   yes   no
- Oarlock sockets close to 10 inches from after edge of center thwart and about 5 to 7 inches above thwart?* (If more than 2 inches from these dimensions, pay extra-careful attention to how comfortable the boat is to row for 15 minutes or so.)   yes   no
- Oarlock sockets attached to solid wood?   yes   no
- Skeg shoe available?   yes   no
- Bottom strakes available?   yes   no
- Mast step apparently well reinforced?   yes   no

*Don't be afraid to take along a tape measure.

Design Considerations

- Is bottom "rockered" to enhance rowing?   yes   no
- Is freeboard high enough for good capacity and dryness in a chop?   yes   no
- Are stern sections flat enough to permit efficient use of outboard motor   yes   no
- Does sailing model have kick-up rudder?   yes   no
- Is sailing rig easy to set up?   yes   no
- Can rig be stored within the boat?   yes   no
- Do sheetleads permit proper sail trim?   yes   no

INFLATABLES

Manufacturer: Achilles
U.S. Headquarters
355 Murray Hill Parkway
East Rutherford, NJ 07073
(201) 438–6400

	LT-2	LT-3DX	LT-4DX	SPD-4AD	SPD-4FL
Length OA	7 ft. 1 in.	8 ft. 4 in.	9 ft. 5 in.	10 ft. 2 in.	10 ft. 2 in.
Length INT	5 ft. 1 in.	6 ft. 3 in.	7 ft. 1 in.	6 ft. 10 in.	7 ft. 3 in.
Beam OA	4 ft.	4 ft. 1 in.	4 ft. 7 in.	4 ft. 9 in.	4 ft. 9 in.
Beam INT	2 ft.	2 ft.	2 ft. 3 in.	2 ft. 3 in.	2 ft. 3 in.
Weight	30 lb.	45 lb.	65 lb.	95 lb.	85 lb.
Dimensions					
(stowed)	31x16x9 in.	38x18x12 in.	42x20x12 in.	46x22x12 in.	41x22x11 in.
Capacity					
(lb./people)	580/2	705/3	990/4	990/4	1,010/4
Max. hp	2	3.5	4	9.9	8
Tube diam.	11.8 in.	12 in.	14.2 in.	15 in.	15 in.
Chambers	2	2	3	3+keel	3+keel
Price	$665	$860	$1,100	$1,460	$1,285

Construction: Achilles boats are built of nylon fabric coated with neoprene inside the tubes (for airtightness) and hypalon outside. The fabrics are of *different weights,* depending on model designation. The seams are cold-glued, reinforced inside and out, and backed by a five-year warranty (except for the LT-2). Plywood floorboards are standard. Oars are aluminum.

Comments: Achilles is a multiline Japanese manufacturer that makes a variety of PVC products, including shoes and automotive moldings, but it has thus far elected to build its boats of nylon/hypalon with cold-glued seams, rather than PVC-coated polyester with fused seams. Differentiating models can be tricky, with some mail-order houses selling the less-expensive boats and dealers the more heavily constructed versions. The chart here illustrates the difference between the identically sized SPD-4AD and SPD-4FL. The AD uses 840-denier fabric versus 420 for the FL. It is a heavier boat and is rated for more horsepower. The top-line Achilles models are worth considering, particularly if there is a good dealer in your area to handle warranty claims and service.

Manufacturer: Avon Inflatables Ltd.
IMTRA Corp.
30 Samuel Barnet Boulevard
New Bedford Industrial Park
New Bedford, MA 02745
(617) 990–2700

	Redstart	Avon 8	Redcrest	Redseal	Redshank
Length OA	8 ft. 2 in.	8 ft. 2 in.	9 ft. 3 in.	10 ft. 3 in.	12 ft. 3 in.
Length INT	5 ft. 10 in.	5 ft. 10 in.	6 ft. 10 in.	7 ft. 10 in.	9 ft. 5 in.
Beam OA	4 ft.	4 ft.	4 ft. 6 in.	4 ft. 10 in.	5 ft. 6 in.
Beam INT	2 ft.	2 ft.	2 ft. 4 in.	2 ft. 6 in.	3 ft.
Weight: boat	36 lb.	36 lb.	43 lb.	51 lb.	62 lb.
Floor	18 lb.	18 lb.	24 lb.	31 lb.	44 lb.
Dimensions					
(stowed)	33 x 18 in.	33 x 18 in.	35 x 22 in.	41 x 20 in.	43 x 20 in.
Capacity					
(lbs./people)	550/3	550/3	700/4	950/5	1,250/7
Max. hp	3	3	4	5	7
Tube diam.	12 in.	12 in.	13 in.	14 in.	15 in.
Chambers	2+thwart	2		2+thwart	
Price	$975	$875	$995	-	-
(Check with dealer/mail order house for prices/discounts.)					

Construction: Boats are nylon coated with hypalon on both sides, using fabric made by Avon and guaranteed against deterioration from aging, cracking, or porosity for 10 years. Construction is cold-glued. Oarlocks are rubber. Optional thwarts are fiberglass. Valves are plastic. Hardware is stainless steel. Floorboards are marine plywood. Oars are wood.

Comments: The largest-selling Avon is the Redcrest, an exceptionally convenient boat in terms of size, weight, and capacity. Avon dinghies have a deservedly excellent reputation for quality. A line of hard-transom boats, the Rovers, is also available for use as tenders and permit higher-horsepower motors to be used. Until somebody proves they build a better boat, and sell it through an organization as widespread as Avon's, and back it with a similar warranty, these inflatables will continue to be top-rated.

Manufacturer: Bombard
U.S. Headquarters
P.O. Box 400
Thompson Creek Road
Stevensville, MD 21666
(301) 643–4141

	AX 1	AX 2	AX 3	AX 4
Length OA	7 ft. 2 in.	7 ft. 11 in.	9 ft. 6 in.	9 ft. 6 in.
Length INT	4 ft. 11 in.	4 ft. 11 in.	6 ft. 5 in.	6 ft. 5 in.
Beam OA	3 ft. 9 in.	3 ft. 9 in.	4 ft. 7 in.	4 ft. 7 in.
Beam INT	1 ft. 8 in.	1 ft. 8 in.	2 ft. 7½ in.	2 ft. 7 ½ in.
Weight	34 lb.	42 lb.	51 lb.	64 lb.
Dimensions				
(stowed)	35 x 16 in.	35 x 16 in.	39½ x 16 in.	39½ x 16 in.
Capacity				
(lb./people)	549/2 or 3	549/3	715/4	715/4
Recommended hp	2	3	3	3
Max. hp	3	4	4	4
Tube diam.	12½ in.	12½ in.	13½ in.	13½ in.
Chambers	2	2	2	2
Price	$650	$820	$960	$1,175

Construction: Fabric is PVC-coated polyester with fused ("thermo-bonded") seams. All but AX 1 have wooden transoms. Wood-slat floorboards are in all but AX 4, which has plywood floorboards. Oars are aluminum.

Comments: A built-in bellows is a nice touch that permits the boats to be topped up conveniently as necessary. A wood or inflatable center thwart must be purchased as an option.

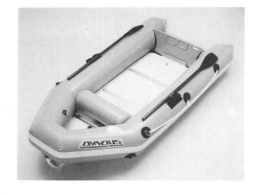

Manufacturer: Dynous
    Inflatable Boats by Toyo
    180 Adams Avenue
    Hauppauge, NY 11788
    (516) 434–8310

	Dynous DX-102	Dynous DX-92	Dynous DF-92	Dynous DL-82
Length OA	10 ft. 2 in.	9 ft. 2 in.	9 ft. 2 in.	8 ft. 2 in.
Beam OA	4 ft. 10 in.	4 ft. 7 in.	4 ft. 7 in.	4 ft. 4 in.
Weight				
(w/floorboards)	86 lb.	79 lb.	82 lb.	50 lb.
Capacity	4	2	3	3
Max. hp	9.9	8	8	4
Chambers	2+thwart	2+thwart	2	2
Price	$1,570	$1,370	$1,370	$920

Construction: These inflatables are built of nylon fabric manufactured by Toyo, a major Japanese tire manufacturer that also supplies fabric to other inflatable makers. The fabric is calendered on the inside with neoprene, on the outside with neoprene and hypalon. The DL, DA, and DF lines have 420-denier fabric, reducing cost and weight. The DX is made of 840-denier fabric. Seams are cold-glued and taped inside and out. The transoms are finished with epoxy paint for enhanced durability and reinforced with a fillet between the transom and the hull tubes. Tongue-and-groove aluminum floorboards are standard on the DX models, covered with nonslip mats. The valves are nylon.

Comments: The neoprene/hypalon coating makes these boats particularly smooth to the touch, and they are said to be notably airtight. An inflatable keel is used and the bottom of the DX and DF models, viewed at the transom, has a noticeable V-shape that improves tracking. The DX line has the most to offer. A 5-year fabric warranty was in effect at the time of publication. These are hard-transom dinghies with many thoughtful touches.

Manufacturer: Harrison-Hoge Industries
    P.O. Box 944
    Smithtown, NY 11787
    (516) 724–8900

	Sea Eagle 250	Sea Eagle 310	Sea Eagle 8
Length	7 ft. 6 in.	9 ft. 4 in.	9 ft. 7 in.
Beam	4 ft.	4 ft. 4 in.	4 ft. 6 in.
Weight	14 lb.	24 lb.	33 lb.
Fabric thickness	22 mil	28 mil	33 mil
Capacity	450 lb.	650 lb.	950 lb.
Max. hp	not rated	not rated	3
Chambers	4	4	5
Price	$60	$140	$240

Construction: These inflatables are made of unsupported PVC with welded seams. The Sea Eagle 8 has a wooden motor mount, floorboards, and stern seat.

Comments: These are only a few from the wide range of models offered. Entirely machine-made and inexpensive compared with the other inflatables listed, Sea Eagles appear to get the job done as an out-and-back dinghy for light-duty and fun use. The configuration of the air chambers, one atop the other, is interesting, and this acts as a safeguard should a chamber be punctured.

Manufacturer: Metzeler
  U.S. Headquarters
  Thompson Creek Road
  P.O. Box 400
  Stevensville, MD 21666
  (301) 269–5822

	Jolly M	Aztek M	Tender I
Length OA	8 ft. 3 in.	9 ft. 6 in.	9 ft. 7 in.
Length INT	5 ft. 5 in.	6 ft. 2 in.	5 ft. 11 in.
Beam OA	4 ft.	4 ft.	4 ft. 10 in.
Beam INT	1 ft. 10 in.	1 ft. 9 in.	2 ft. 2 in.
Weight	31 lb.	38 lb.	58 lb.
Dimensions			
(stowed)	25 x 22 x 7 in.	29 x 17 x 9 in.	31 x 19 x 13 in.
Capacity			
(lb./people)	660/3	770/3	880/4
Recommended hp	2	5	6
Chambers	4	4	4
Price	$985	$1,185	$1,655

Construction: Previously made of polyester fabric coated with natural rubber inside and hypalon outside, these boats are to be built with polyester/PVC and fused-seam construction now that Zodiac has purchased the company. Boats have wooden transoms bolted to rubber fittings on the hull.

Comments: Dealers and repair shops with whom the author spoke were not particularly impressed with the fabric of previous models. The inflatable floors add stiffness to the boat, enhancing performance with either oars or motor. These are interesting boats worth investigating, but discussion with owners and inflatable service shops is recommended.

Manufacturer: Sillinger USA
15001 North Hayden Road
Scottsdale, AZ 85260
(602) 948–0944

	TRS 245 GTX	**TRS 280 GTX**
Length OA	8 ft. 2 in.	9 ft. 2 in.
Beam OA	4 ft. 4 in.	4 ft. 3 in.
Weight	40 lb.	62 lb.
Dimensions		
(stowed)	39 x 21 x 9 in.	42 x 24 x 14 in.
Capacity		
(lbs./people)	838/3 or 4	904/4
Recommended hp	4	5
Max. hp	6	7
Tube diam.	15 in.	15 in.
Chambers	2	2
Price	Check with importer/dealers.	

Construction: Fabric is 1100-decitex hypalon-coated nylon with cold-glued seams. "Sillinger is the only French manufacturer to exclusively use the manual assembly method for its entire product range," says the catalog. Black rubber fittings, stainless rings. These are hard-transom dinghies with wood slat floorboards. The thwart is fabric. Oars are aluminum.

Comments: These nice-looking boats reflect excellent materials and craftsmanship. They are primarily intended for use with an outboard. The dealer network is growing. Sillinger has been in and out of the U.S. market in the past.

Manufacturer: Zodiac
  U.S. Headquarters
  Thompson Creek Road
  Stevensville, MD 21666
  (301) 269–5822

	T 240	T 280
Length OA	7 ft. 10 in.	9 ft. 2 in.
Length INT	5 ft. 3 in.	6 ft. 7 in.
Beam OA	4 ft. 11 in.	4 ft. 11 in.
Beam INT	2 ft. 4 in.	2 ft. 4 in.
Weight	46 lb.	51 lb.
Dimensions		
(stowed)	41 x 19 x 9 in.	41 x 19 x 9 in.
Capacity		
(lbs./people)	661/3	882/4
Max. hp	4	4
Tube diam.	16 in.	16 in.
Chambers	2	2
Price	$695	$895

Construction: Boats are made of 1100-decitex polyester coated with Strongan, a kind of polyvinyl chloride (PVC) with fused seams using sealing strips both inside and out. Floor slats are standard. The T 240 is a soft-stern dinghy; the T 280 has a wooden transom.

Comments: The Cadet models, a similar-looking range of hard-transom boats (7 feet 10 inches to 10 feet 2 inches), are also available.

PRAMS

Manufacturer: The Back 'n Forth Co.
42 Gann Road
East Hampton, NY 11937
(516) 324–6393

	Uqbar 6	Uqbar 7	Uqbar 8	Uqbar 10
Length	5 ft. 11 in.	6 ft. 10 in.	7 ft. 10 in.	9 ft. 10 in.
Beam	3 ft. 10 in.	4 ft.	4 ft.	4 ft. 9 in.
Capacity	2 adults	2 adults+	3 adults+	4 adults+
Weight	35 lb.	42 lb.	55 lb.	72 lb.
Rig		sprit	sprit	sprit
		32 sq. ft.	32 sq. ft.	55 sq. ft.
Designer	Redjeb Jordania			
Price (kit)	$249	$269	$289	$389
		(sailing versions add $225-$345)		
Complete boat				
(row/sail)	$437	$457/$668	$547/$958	$667/$1,158

Construction: Marine plywood/epoxy, stitch-and-glue. A chine with its changing bevels is not required, thus eliminating one stumbling block for amateur builders.

Comments: Pronounced "Ook-Bar," these prams offer a most interesting alternative for anyone looking for lightweight, comparatively low-cost dinghies. The 6 and 7 are particularly intriguing because of their roominess for their size and their light weight. The sprit rig makes sense, as does the leeboard of the 7. The larger models have daggerboards. The kit version would make an excellent first-boat building project that should result in a useful dinghy.

Manufacturer: Britannia Boats Ltd.
  P.O. Box 5033
  Annapolis, MD 21403
  (301) 269–6617

	6 Ft. 8 In.	7 Ft. 10 In.
Length	6 ft. 8 in.	7 ft. 10 in.
Beam	4 ft. 2 in.	4 ft. 2 in.
Weight	60 lb.	75 lb.
Max. hp	2	2
Rig	gunter	gunter
	30 sq. ft.	40 sq. ft.
Price	$835	$930
	(plus about $300 for a rig and $55 to $90 shipping)	

Construction: A folding dinghy made of marine plywood with nylon hinges, galvanized oarlocks.

Comments: Built in England, these dinghies are only 4¼ inches thick and about 20 inches wide when folded. Despite the folding feature, these prams have a not-unpleasing shape, and tests in the British yachting press suggest they row and sail well. A skeg wheel is built in to aid handling ashore. The boats are quick to fold and unfold. No buoyancy is built in, but foam buoyancy is available as an option and probably should be considered necessary, although it inevitably adds a certain complication to this clever boat.

Manufacturer: Faering Design
  Route 1, Box 223
  Suttons Bay, MI 49682
  (616) 271–6729

	8-Foot Pram	10-Foot Pram
Length	8 ft.	10 ft.
Beam	4 ft.	4 ft.
Weight	75 lb. (row)	95 lb. (sail)
Rig	standing lug	standing lug
	28 sq. ft.	36 sq. ft.
Designer	modified L. F. Herreshoff/Norwegian pram	
Price (row/sail)	$2,900/$3,650	$3,300/$4,075

Construction: Wood construction, lapstrake, white cedar over white oak; mahogany transom, thwarts, and trim; copper rivet fasteners. Bottom protected by bilge strips and half-oval brass keel shoe. Oars are custom made of Sitka spruce and are leathered.

Comments: These are beautifully made boats that should last a long time, given proper care. The builder has combined the elegant, comparatively fine lines of Norwegian prams with the fuller sections of the Francis Herreshoff boats to create a handsome, burdensome craft. A proper dinghy.

Manufacturer: New England Skiff
  P.O. Box 267
  Wakefield, RI 02880
  (401) 789–4609

	Puddleduck
Length	7 ft. 10 in.
Beam	4 ft. 0 in.
Weight: wood seats/trim	95 lb.
fiberglass seats	65 lb.
Max. hp	2
Rig	fixed gunter, 34 sq. ft.
Designer	Robert Baker
Price	$750/$1,550

Construction: Hand lay-up: 20 mils of gelcoat reinforced with two layers of 1½-ounce matt and a layer of 10-ounce boatcloth. A fiberglass liner version is available, intended primarily for sailing programs.

Comments: Originally designed for plywood construction and a sailing program at St. George's School, the Puddleduck proved to be an excellent sailor. The fiberglass version retains that ability, something that cannot be said for many small dinghies. The boat and rig are built entirely by Jonathan and Nicole Nomer, hardware being the only bought-out parts. A good small dinghy, one of the few fiberglass prams on the market, and an interesting price bracket.

Manufacturer: E. Tyler Proctor, Jr.
16 Shannon Road
Bar Harbor, ME 04609
(207) 288–3679

	8-Foot Pram	**10-Foot Pram**
Length	8 ft. 4 in.	10 ft.
Beam	4 ft. 6 in.	4 ft.
Weight	95 lb.	110 lb.
Max. hp	1½	2
Rig	lug, 50 sq. ft.	lug, 60 sq. ft.
Designer	Herreshoff/Proctor	Herreshoff/Gardner
Price	$1,900	$3,500

Construction: Cedar planks, oak frames, copper and bronze fasteners and hardware.

Comments: These are two sensible and useful prams with highly practical rigs. The 8-foot pram is a stock boat at the shop. The 10-footer was modified by John Gardner from an L. Francis Herreshoff design.

Manufacturer: Rivendell Marine
125 Lagoon Road
Bend Boat Basin
Melville, RI 02840
(401) 683–1107

	Hobbit Pram
Length	8 ft.
Beam	4 ft.
Weight	95 lb.
Rig	sprit
	29 sq. ft.
Designer	based on
	Herreshoff and Culler
Price	
row/sail	$3,750/$4,500

Construction: These boats are built of white cedar planking over white-oak keels and frames. Copper rivets and silicon-bronze fasteners are used.

Comments: Rivendell proprietor Tom Wolstenholme and some expert boatwrights have been building dinghies, and restoring/repairing larger boats, for more than a decade. The craftsmanship of this shop is exquisite.

Manufacturer: RKL Boatworks
  Mount Desert, ME 04660
  (207) 244–5997 (day)
  (207) 244–3706 (night)

Pram Tender	
Length	8 ft.
Beam	3 ft. 10 in.
Depth	1 ft. 5 in.
Capacity	450 lb.
Weight	70 lb.
Rig	marconi
	45 sq. ft.
	2-pc. wood mast
Designer	after L.F. Herreshoff
Price	check with builder

Construction: Available in either fiberglass—hand lay-up—with mahogany trim or strip-planked, WEST System construction. Two sets of oarlock sockets are provided. A brass keel band is standard.

Comments: Bob Lincoln has steadfastly and patiently carved out a business for himself, building and selling small craft. The craftsmanship is excellent. Sailing performance of the lightweight cold-molded pram should be exceptional. This pram reportedly tows well. Contact the builder for more details.

Manufacturer: Stephen Wilce Boats
   P.O. Box 962
   Winters, CA 95694
   (916) 795–4816

	Buttercup
Length	7 ft. 9 in.
Beam	3 ft. 7 in.
Weight	
(row/sail)	38/38 lb.(hull only)
Max. hp	2
Rig	marconi/sprit boom
	40 sq. ft.
Designer	Stephen Wilce
Price	
(row/sail)	$680/$1,170

Construction: This and other Wilce boats are built of Sealight—a sandwich material of foam and a thermoplastic "alloy" called Kydex, which forms the outer skins. The material used is about 2 inches thick, a dimension that yields strength comparable to that of ¼-inch plywood or .10-inch-thick fiberglass. However, Sealight results in an unsinkable boat that is also comparatively lightweight. The material can be dented in hard use but is repairable with epoxy paste.

Comments: New boatbuilding materials and ideas don't appear frequently, but Sealight represents an interesting alternative to other construction types. Like plywood, the material permits use of rather large, unsupported panels bendable in one direction. The Sealight boats are all hard-chine types. Buttercup has two sets of oarlock sockets and all these dinghies have foot stretchers to enhance rowing efficiency. The oarlocks on the larger models appear to be mounted outside the gunwale; some provision for a gunwale guard would be necessary.

HARD-CHINE DINGHIES

(including cathedral hulls and trihulls)

Manufacturer: American Sail, Inc.
7350 Pepperdam Avenue
Charleston, SC 29418
(803) 552–8548

	8-Foot Dink	**8-Foot Trihull**
Length	8 ft. 1 in.	8 ft. 1 in.
Beam	4 ft. 3 in.	4 ft. 3 in.
Depth	1 ft. 8 in.	1 ft. 3 in.
Weight		
(row/sail)	85/90 lb.	95 lb.
Capacity	390 lb.	390 lb.
Max. hp	2	2
Rig	marconi	
	35 sq. ft	
Price		
(row/sail)	$695/$1,150	$795

Construction: Hand-laid-up fiberglass with gelcoated liner and flanged gunwale with vinyl guard. Flotation is located both in the hull's sides and in forward and aft tanks. A wood motor-mount block is provided. Oarlock sockets are chrome with nylon inserts to protect against wear.

Comments: The 8-foot Dink is a hard-chine dinghy with hull liner that has a nonskid finish, a nice touch. There is no provision for rowing from the bow. The sailing model's middle thwart benefits from support in its center from the daggerboard trunk.

Manufacturer: Boston Whaler
   1149 Hingham Street
   Rockland, MA 02370
   (617) 871–1400

Tender	
Length	9 ft.
Beam	4 ft. 4 in.
Weight	140 lb.
Capacity	600 lb.
Max. hp	5
Price	check with dealer

Construction: Specially designed chopper guns spray 3-inch strands of fiber into gelcoated molds; the chopped matt is then rolled out with rollers and brushes to eliminate air bubbles. Each boat is composed of an inner and an outer shell, joined while wet; the space between the shells is filled with polyurethane foam. The whole forms a single unit of great strength.

Comments: Offering best performance with an outboard, the Whaler is nicely manufactured, and its construction method (and unsinkability) has been well proven.

Manufacturer: Criterion Co., Inc.
   494 Milford Road
   Swansea, MA 02777
   (617) 678–8681

	Model 72	Model 84
Length	7 ft. 2 in.	8 ft. 4 in.
Beam	4 ft.	4 ft.
Weight	70 lb.	80 lb.
Max. hp	2	2
Rig		marconi, 41 sq. ft.
Price	check with builder	

Construction: Hand-laid fiberglass with flanged gunwale. Models 72 and 84 are hard-chine, V-bottomed boats.

Comments: Low-cost, all-fiberglass dinghies. Trihull soft-chine models are also available.

Manufacturer: Dyer Boats
   The Anchorage
   57 Miller Street
   Warren, RI 02885
   (401) 245–3300

	Midget Lo-Sheer	Midget Hi-Sheer	Dhow	*Dink "D"
Length	7 ft. 9 in.	7 ft. 11 in.	9 ft.	10 ft.
Beam	3 ft. 11 in.	4 ft. 11 in.	4 ft. 6 in.	4 ft. 6½ in.
Weight: row	81 lb.	83 lb.	104 lb.	125 lb.
sail	88 lb.	90 lb.	106 lb.	135 lb.
Depth	17½ in.	20 in.	21 in.	22¼ in.
Max. cap.	380 lb.	465 lb.	650 lb.	740 lb.
Rig	sliding gunter	sliding gunter	marconi	marconi
Designer	Philip Rhodes/ Bill Dyer			
Price	check with builder			

*The Dink "D" is a round-bilged boat, but is mentioned here for completeness of the Dyer description.

Construction: Construction involves hand lay-up of two layers of cloth followed by four pieces of matt and two more layers of cloth, with each layer allowed to dry before the next is added. According to the builder, that contributes to the boats' attractive finish, because less heat is generated during lamination. Stainless and custom bronze hardware is used, as are riveted oak gunwales.

Comments: Today's Dyer dinghies are the result of traditions that date back to before World War II. The 10-footer became the largest active class in the North American Dinghy Association in the 1930s. Originally lapstrake, it was changed to a smooth-sided boat when postwar production in fiberglass commenced. The 9-foot "Dhow," originally designed for mass production in plywood, was developed for use aboard PT boats. The first fiberglass Dhow was molded in 1949. The 7-foot 9-inch Midget was developed for easy stowage aboard a Concordia yawl. The 7-foot 11-inch model offers greater freeboard and is the most popular Dyer dinghy. The Midgets are lightweight compared with some other 8-footers, yet are reasonably durable. A second set of oarlocks for the bow seat, and a bow seat well positioned for rowing, are notable features. Although the Midgets' design has been much copied, their full bows and construction quality continue to make them a standard against which others are judged. The larger boats face stiffer competition. The 10-footer is a pleasant boat to sail. Dyer dinghies are sold by an extensive dealer network, and their resale value is usually excellent.

Manufacturer: Eli Laminates
  1439 Montauk Highway
  Oakdale, NY 11769
  (516) 589–4020

	Scout	Scout	Scout	Trihull	Trihull
Length	7 ft.	8 ft.	9½ ft.	7 ft.	8 ft.
Beam	4 ft.	4 ft.	4 ft. 4 in.	4 ft. 2 in.	4 ft. 3 in.
Depth	17 in.	18 in.	22 in.	17 in.	21 in.
Weight	65 lb.	72 lb.	110 lb.	79 lb.	85 lb.
Capacity	373 lb.	445 lb.	495 lb.	465 lb.	598 lb.
Max. hp	2	2	2	2	2
Rig		marconi	marconi		
		39 sq. ft.	49 sq. ft.		
Price					
(row/sail)	$445	$495/$725	$575/$795	$495	$545

Construction: Hand-laid fiberglass with flanged gunwale. One set of oarlock sockets is fitted. Sailing versions have daggerboards.

Comments: Begun in a garage, Eli Laminates eventually grew enough to warrant building its own factory. The production method of building a run of one model at a time helps control costs and prices. These are basic dinghies.

Manufacturer: Ensign Dinghies & Marine
Michael Dapice Enterprises, Inc.
P.O. Box 547
Rye, NY 10580
(914) 967–1656

	Sea Lion	Shipmate
Length	7 ft.	8 ft. 1 in.
Beam	4 ft. 1 in.	3 ft. 10 in.
Depth	1 ft. 5 in.	1 ft. 7 in.
Capacity	375 lb.	375 lb.
Weight	75 lb.	80 lb.
Max. hp	2	2
Rig	marconi	marconi
	36 sq. ft.	42 sq. ft.
Designer	Mike Dapice	
Price		
(row/sail)	$429/$689	$489/$799

Construction: Fiberglass construction that involves both chopped matt and hand-laid 24-ounce woven roving. Fittings are backed by hardwood blocks glassed in place.

Comments: Ensign builds several other dinghy models, including catamaran types, in addition to those listed here. The boats are priced toward the lower end of the market. Designer/builder Mike Dapice has extensive experience in the small-boat business and a wide dealer network. Don't expect to get everything at these prices, but the boats have some nice touches and are covered by a two-year warranty.

Manufacturer: Leisure Life Limited
   3800 Patterson Avenue, S.E.
   Grand Rapids, MI 49508
   (616) 949–0866

	Water Tender 9	Water Tender 10
Length	8 ft. 6 in.	9 ft. 2 in.
Beam	3 ft. 10 in.	4 ft. 7 in.
Weight	95 lb.	106 lb.
Capacity	-	552 lb.
Max. hp	2	5
Price	$375	$465

Construction: These boats are molded of high-density polyethylene, hull and liner. Foam flotation is installed. Two sets of oarlock sockets are provided.

Comments: A trihedral hull design that should yield good performance with an outboard. The aesthetics of polyethylene—a durable, low-maintenance material—must remain a subjective matter.

Manufacturer: Lee Fiberglass Products
   P.O. Box 149
   Winthrop, ME 04364
   (207) 395–4797

	Scottie
Length	8 ft.
Beam	4 ft.
Depth	1 ft. 4 in.
Weight	80 lb.
Rig	
Price	$480

Construction: Fiberglass with flanged gunwale and varnished mahogany seats.

Comments: Low-cost fiberglass boats.

Manufacturer: Livingston, Inc.
  25 37th Street NE
  Auburn, WA 98001
  (206) 852–7374

	7.5	**9**	**10**
Length	7 ft. 5 in.	9 ft.	10 ft.
Beam	4 ft. 5 in.	4 ft. 5 in.	5 ft. 2 in.
Capacity	450 lb.	550 lb.	700 lb.
Max. hp	5	8	10-15
Rig	marconi	marconi	marconi
Price (approx.)	$489	$599	$789

Construction: Boats are a combination of "hand-laid roving and precision applied random fibers" with flanged gunwales. Stainless keel strips are available.

Comments: These are cathedral-hulled boats intended primarily for motoring. They have comparatively generous freeboard and carrying capacity.

Lowell tender (see page 150).

Manufacturer: Lowell's Boat Shop
   450 Main Street
   Amesbury, MA 01913
   (617) 388–0162

	Tender	Tender	Tender
Length	8 ft. 9 in.	10 ft.	12 ft.
Beam	4 ft. 3 in.	4 ft. 3 in.	4 ft. 4 in.
Depth	1 ft. 2½ in.	1 ft. 3 in.	1 ft. 3½ in.
Weight	Approx. 100-150 lbs., check w/builder		
Rig	gunter	gunter	gunter
	32 sq.ft.	42 sq. ft.	60 sq. ft.
Designer	Lowell's Boat Shop		
Price			
(Row/Sail)	$2982/$4115	$3055/$4185	$3305/$4450

Construction: Boats are lapstrake, cedar over oak, four planks per side. Mahogany transoms and seats and oak rails are fitted. The bottom and garboards are epoxy-sealed and covered with a layer of 10-ounce fiberglass cloth. Two sets of bronze oarlocks are fitted. Unpainted models are available at a significant saving in price. Sprit rigs are available if preferred.

Comments: These revised versions of the Lowell tenders are fuller and more stable than those previously built, offering some increase in capacity. Modifications can be made at the customer's request, and very nice pram versions of the skiffs are also available in seven-, eight-, or nine-foot lengths. The prams are notable for their capacity and good, dry, towing performance. These are sturdy, handsome boats that require modest maintenance. Owned and operated by Jim Odell and his son George, Lowell's is the oldest boatshop in the country and is still turning out sturdy and honest wooden boats that are very popular with their owners.

Manufacturer: Open Sea Inc.
   Nauticat Chesapeake
   P.O. Box 487
   Solomons Island, MD 20688
   (301) 261–9005

	Terhi 245	Baby Fun
Length	7 ft. 11 in.	7 ft. 9 in.
Beam	4 ft. 1 in.	4 ft. 3 in.
Weight	88 lb.	115 lb.
Max. hp	2	4
Price	$665	$735

Construction: These boats are molded of an ABS thermoplastic hull and liner with polyurethane foam sandwiched in between. A single set of oarlock sockets is fitted.

Comments: Imported from Finland.

Manufacturer: Porta-Bote International
   The Porta-Bote Building
   1074 Independence Avenue
   Mountain View, CA 94043
   (415) 961–5334

	8 Feet	**10 Feet**	**12 Feet**
Length	8 ft.	10 ft.	12 ft.
Beam	4 ft. 10 in.	5 ft.	5 ft.
Depth	1 ft. 8 in.	1 ft. 9 in.	1 ft. 10 in.
Weight	49 lb.	59 lb.	69 lb.
Capacity	325 lb.	475 lb.	610 lb.
Max. engine wt.	24 lb.	40 lb.	50 lb.
Price	$859	$879	$899

Construction: The boats are made of 1/4-inch-thick polypropylene. The hull material is warranteed for 10 years.

Comments: The boat folds to a sailboardlike package 22 inches wide. It has foam flotation and meets Coast Guard standards, according to the manufacturer. A sailing rig is available and includes a leeboard. Marketed as much, or more, to hunters and fishermen as to those looking for a dinghy, the Porta-Bote offers a combination of inflatable convenience and rigid-dinghy performance. This is an intriguing alternative to more conventional dinghies.

Manufacturer: Rivendell Marine
   125 Lagoon Road
   Bend Boat Basin
   Melville, RI 02840
   (401) 683–1107

Skiff	
Length	10 ft.
Beam	4 ft.
Weight	100 lb.
Rig	sprit/sliding gunter
	55 sq. ft.
Designer	William/John Atkin
Price	
(row/sail)	$1,000/$1,750

Construction: These boats are built of white-cedar planking over white-oak keels and frames. Copper rivets and silicon-bronze fasteners are used.

Comments: Rivendell proprietor Tom Wolstenholme and some expert boatwrights have been building dinghies, and restoring/repairing larger boats, for more than a decade. The craftsmanship of this shop is exquisite. The Atkin skiff brings this level of craftsmanship and a handsome and serviceable dinghy to a price range comparable to that of many fiberglass boats.

Manufacturer: The Rockport Apprenticeshop
   P.O. Box 359 (Sea Street)
   Rockport, ME 04856
   (207) 236–6071

Susan Skiff	
Length	11 ft. 3 in.
Beam	4 ft. 5 in.
Depth	1 ft. 3 in.
Weight	150 lb.
Rig	lug
Designer	Bob Steward
Price	
(row/sail):	$950/$1,450

Construction: Cedar planked on oak frames with a cross-planked bottom. The outside is painted; the interior is oiled.

Comments: In Bob Steward's words, Susan "fills the need for a rowboat that will be easier to propel than one of the minimum length dinghies, especially when loaded with a second person and gear." The Apprenticeshop has been building the Susan since the mid 1970s, and has built more than 100 of them to date. The Susan is a first project for boatbuilding apprentices, enabling the shop to offer these pretty boats for sale at a most reasonable price. Plans and a how-to-build manual are available for the home builder. The Rockport Apprenticeshop also offers for sale a wide range of other classic wooden small craft, and will build any small boat on commission. Average time to completion from receipt of order is six to nine months. Workmanship is first-rate.

Manufacturer: Snug Harbor Boat Works
  10121 Snug Harbor Road
  St. Petersburg, FL 33702
  (813) 576–1094

	6 Feet 10 Inches	8 Feet	Captain's Gig
Length	6 ft. 10 in.	8 ft.	10 ft.
Beam	3 ft. 11 in.	4 ft.	4 ft. 6 in.
Weight	90 lb.	110 lb.	150 lb.
Capacity	415 lb.	500 lb.	675 lb.
Max. hp	2	2	2
Rig		marconi	
		42 sq. ft.	
Designer	Ross A. Sackett		
Price	check with manufacturer/dealer		

Construction: Fiberglass construction using hull liner and flanged gunwale.

Comments: A hard-chine dinghy. The through-seat and hull drains and stern lifting handles are a nice touch.

Manufacturer: Starwing
  500 Wood Street
  P.O. Box 137
  Bristol, RI 02809
  (401) 254–0670

	Deck Hand	Harpooner
Length	7 ft. 2 in.	8 ft.
Beam	3 ft. 11 in.	4 ft.
Weight	65 lb.	90 lb.
Capacity	390 lb.	475 lb.
Rig	rowing only	rowing only
Price	$499	$739

Construction: Fiberglass construction that combines chopped matt with a layer of woven roving laid in by hand, and woven roving reinforcement in the flanged gunwale for extra rigidity. An exclusive rubrail, which the builder claims is particularly durable, is installed. It is a soft vinyl that is heated and stretched over the hull flange. Nice touches include a PVC shoe bonded to the skeg with epoxy. A repair kit is available to replace the PVC strip, but this must be done before the gelcoat is abraded away. Nonskid interior surfaces, a large bow seat, and two sets of bronze oarlocks. The 8-foot Harpooner model has a trihull shape and a hull liner.

Comments: These are nice-looking and neatly finished dinghies, moderate in price. The rubrail is an interesting touch, as is the effort to provide a bow rowing position, useful when the dinghy is fully loaded with people and gear. Long term, some support for the teak center thwart might well be a plus.

Manufacturer: Stephen Wilce Boats
  P.O. Box 962
  Winters, CA 95694
  (916) 795–4816

	Arrowhead 10	Wildflower
Length	9 ft. 10 in.	11 ft. 2 in.
Beam	4 ft. 6 in.	4 ft. 7 in.
Weight		
(row/sail)	60/77 lb.	85/105 lb.
Max. hp	2	2
Rig	marconi/sprit boom	marconi/sprit boom
	50 sq. ft.	60 sq. ft.
Designer	Stephen Wilce	
Price		
(row/sail)	$980/$1,690	$1,380/$1,860

Construction: These and other Wilce boats are built of Sealight—a sandwich material of foam and a thermoplastic "alloy" called Kydex, which forms the outer skins. The material used is about 2 inches thick, a dimension that yields strength comparable to that of 1/4-inch plywood or .10-inch-thick fiberglass. However, Sealight results in an unsinkable boat that is also comparatively lightweight. The material can be dented in hard use but is repairable with epoxy paste.

Comments: New boatbuilding materials and ideas don't appear frequently, but Sealight represents an interesting alternative to other construction types. Like plywood, the material permits use of rather large, unsupported panels bendable in one direction. The Sealight boats are all hard-chine types. Buttercup has two sets of oarlock sockets and all these dinghies have foot stretchers to enhance rowing efficiency. The oarlocks on the larger models appear to be mounted outside the gunwale; some provision for a gunwale guard would be necessary.

Manufacturer: Sumner Boat Co., Inc.
334 South Bayview Avenue
Amityville, NY 11701
(516) 264–1830

	Sumner 7	Sumner 8	Sumner 9
Length	7 ft.	7 ft. 11 in.	9 ft.
Beam	4 ft.	4 ft.	4 ft. 4½ in.
Weight	80 lb.	90 lb.	105 lb.
Capacity	470 lb.	510 lb.	726 lb.
Max. hp	2	2	2
Rig	gunter	gunter	gunter
	39 sq. ft.	39 sq. ft.	54 sq. ft.
Designer	Arthur Sumner		
Price			
(row/sail)	$599/$899	$649/$949	$799/$1,174

Construction: These dinghies are of chopped-matt construction with either a contiguous liner bonded to the hull with resin and flanged gunwales (L models) or a wooden gunwale (W models). The newer L version has somewhat less deadrise (V-angle) to the bottom. Longitudinal flotation and movable thwarts, permitting the boat to be kept properly trimmed, are used.

Two sets of oarlock sockets are provided. The sailing version is equipped with leeboards.

Comments: The use of a liner gives these boats a particularly well-finished look and eliminates the need to varnish the wooden gunwales of the W models. The price is the same for either boat, so the choice is up to the buyer. The removable thwarts permit occupants to adopt the "lifeboat position" and sit on the dinghy's bottom, adding stability if necessary. Leeboards eliminate the daggerboard trunk and the sliding gunter rig replaces the previous sprit rig.

Manufacturer: Tiger Enterprises
 RFD #1, Box 886
 Addison, ME 04606
 (207) 493–6000

DeAvila Cub	
Length	8 ft.
Beam	4 ft. 4 in.
Weight	89 lb.
Capacity	475 lb.
Max. hp	2
Designer	Pat Davis
Price	approx. $500

Construction: "Lapstrake" hand-laid fiberglass roving and matt with a particularly thick flange at the gunwale and a rubber gunwale guard.

Comments: A very sturdy-looking boat.

Manufacturers:
B & S Corp.
Harrison C. Sylvester
Bessey Ridge Road
Albion, ME 04910
(207) 437–9245

Frederick R. Brown
18 Forbes Street
Westboro, MA 01581
(617) 366–7834

	Whitehall	Whitehall
Length	10 ft.	12 ft.
Beam	4 ft.	4 ft. 5 in.
Weight (row/sail)	100/120 lb.	155/170 lb.
Rig	sprit 44 sq. ft.	gaff 78 sq. ft.
		sprit 66 sq. ft.
Max. hp	2	2
Designer	Harry Sylvester has modified an old	
	Whitehall for fiberglass construction.	
Price (row/sail)	$945/$1,445	$1,395/$2,295 (sprit)
		$2,495 (gaff)

Construction: Hand-laid fiberglass hulls with mahogany gunwales and seats. Bronze hardware. Soft gunwale guards and leathered oars are optional.

Comments: The design of the 12-footer is unaltered from the original, which is now on display at the Maine Maritime Museum. The 10-footer has reduced deadrise for greater stability on its shorter length, but the skeg has been shaped to create what is essentially a double-ender below the waterline, enhancing rowing performance because the boat's entry and exit create comparatively little turbulence. These are fine boats built by a company that has steadfastly adhered to principles of quality in adapting proven designs to fiberglass. The sprit rigs offer good performance with a short mast.

Manufacturer: Bauteck Marine
Corporation, Inc.
2060 Dobbs Road
St. Augustine, FL 32086
(904) 824–8826

Bauer 10	
Length	10 ft. 1 in.
Beam	4 ft. 9 in.
Weight	120 lb. (160 lb. rigged)
Capacity	750 lb.
Rig	marconi, 53 sq. ft. (main/jib)
Designer	Hans-Christof Bauer
Price	base prices approx. $1,700-$2,000

Construction: Fiberglass hull, rudder, and centerboard, stainless hardware.

Comments: This is a big, heavy, and able-looking dinghy. Comparatively high freeboard enhances carrying capacity and performance. A keel/skeg shoe is optional. The oars can be locked in the boat with a stainless yoke, a nice touch. Sailing performance seems to be emphasized and the boat is equipped with one set of oarlock sockets. The foam flotation, listed as an option on the literature I received, should be standard.

Manufacturer: R.K. Bentley and Sons, Ltd.
502 31st Street
Newport Beach, CA 92663
(714) 675–4684

	New Spiffy Dink 7 Ft. 3 In.	New Spiffy Dink 8 Ft.
Length	7 ft. 3 in.	8 ft.
Beam	3 ft. 4 in.	4 ft. 1 in.
Depth	1 ft. 8 in.	1 ft. 9 in.
Weight (row/sail)	70/85 lb.	85/100 lb.
Capacity	500 lb.	750 lb.
Rig	marconi, 40 sq. ft.	marconi, 40 sq. ft.
Designer	Hetrick, Hicks, and Bentley	
Price (row/sail)	$775/$1,175	$825/$1,375

Construction: Hand-laid fiberglass matt and cloth with extra glass in the keel
and skeg. A ⅝-inch-thick mahogany transom is bonded to the glass during
lay-up. A mahogany gunwale is used, with guard optional. Two sets of
oarlock sockets are provided.

Comments: A high bow, an extra inch or so of freeboard compared to some
dinghies in this size range, and molded-in lapstrakes promise to make these
comparatively dry, able tenders. Capacity is relatively high—they're "big for
their size." Side flotation tanks, plus flotation in the bow, suggest the Spiffy
Dink will have no problem with level-flotation requirements and it should be
easy to right if capsized. However, there's likely to be quite a tangle of legs
when rowing with a passenger in the stern, as the side tanks reduce space.
Sailing models are equipped with a leeboard, thus eliminating a space-

consuming and potentially leaky daggerboard trunk. Leeboard dinghies are often excellent sailors, and the designer has purposely made both rudder and leeboard of generous dimensions, which should contribute to the responsiveness of the boat. The rig is that of the Sabot dinghy, popular in many countries, should a long-distance cruiser ever need a part. Kit boats are available at significant savings.

Manufacturer: Cape Breton Boatyard Ltd.
　Box 247, Baddeck
　Nova Scotia, Canada B0E 1B0
　(092) 295–2664

Bras d'Or Tender	
Length	12 ft.
Beam	4 ft. 4 in.
Weight	190 lb.
Designer	based on wooden rowboat built in the 1920s at
	Alexander Graham Bell boatshop on the Bras d'Or Lakes
Price	check with builder

Construction: Hand-laid "lapstrake" fiberglass with wooden gunwales.

Comments: A stoutly built boat, this tender is equipped with 7-foot oars, two sets of oarlock sockets, and a boat cover.

Manufacturer: Cape Cod Shipbuilding
　Narrows Road, Box 152
　Wareham, MA 02571
　(617) 295–3550

MK Dinghy	
Length	9 ft. 1½ in.
Beam	4 ft.
Weight(row/sail)	98/125 lb.
Depth	18 in.
Rig	marconi, 48 sq. ft.
	(jointed mast avail.)
Design	originated during World War II as a
	Navy crash-boat tender and for use
	aboard salvage vessels
Price (row/sail)	approx. $825/$1,500

Construction: Boat is built of two hand-laid layers of fiberglass matt—¾ ounce and 1½ ounces. The matt runs from sheer to keel on either side, overlapping at the centerline. The lay-up procedure avoids use of fiberglass roving, which the builders believe would add too much weight.

A unique separate deck piece is laid up in a separate mold. It and the hull mold are then bolted together, and the joint reinforced by fiberglass strips. The deck essentially reinforces the entire hull, and a very sturdy gunwale is thus created, to which a plastic rubrail is glued. This construction method was developed by Cape Cod Shipbuilding.

Rowing models have foam-filled flotation tanks; sailing models have integral air tanks tested at three p.s.i. Rather than drill into the tank area for the bow-eye attachment, the MK has its painter fed through a hole in the breasthook. The center thwart is fiberglass, attached to the hull over a wide area to spread out impact loads.

Comments: This boat is reasonably light for its size. It is an excellent rowboat, improved by the builder's switch from functional if cheap-looking nylon rowlocks to ones cast of bronze. The hull is handsome, although some odd color combinations occasionally appear. The dinghy is built by a manufacturer that advertises seldom but was among the pioneers of fiberglass construction, and it offers a range of boats that share good basic design as a common feature.

Manufacturer: Classic Marine
2244 Main Street
Suite 3
Chula Vista, CA 92011
(619) 423–0206

	7 Feet	8 Feet	10 Feet
Length	7 ft.	8 ft.	10 ft.
Beam	3 ft. 11 in.	3 ft. 11 in.	3 ft. 11 in.
Weight	60 lb.	70 lb.	90 lb.
Rig	marconi	marconi	marconi
	40 sq. ft.	45 sq. ft.	55 sq. ft.
Price: Classic	$895	$995	$1,095
La Playa	$1,250	$1,350	$1,550

Construction: Hand-laid "lapstrake" fiberglass with mahogany motor pad and wood gunwales. Gelcoat finish inside and out. Stainless fittings and mahogany trim on Classic, "brass" and teak on La Playa. The Classic models are about 5 pounds lighter than the La Playas. Only one set of oarlock sockets is fitted. Gunwale guards and a halyard are optional, as is a stainless steel rubbing strake.

Comments: The lighter weight of the Classic models has appeal. Feedback from the owner of a 10-foot Classic model suggests nice rowing performance with sailing ability enhanced by stronger breezes. Reinforcement of the mast step was needed.

Manufacturer: Criterion Co., Inc.
494 Milford Road
Swansea, MA 02777
(617) 678–8681

Model 73	
Length	7 ft.
Beam	4 ft. 5 in.
Weight	75 lb.
Price	check with builder

Construction: Hand-laid fiberglass with flanged gunwale.

Comments: Low-cost, all-fiberglass dinghies. A soft-chine 10-footer is also available.

Manufacturer: Ensign Dinghies & Marine
Michael Dapice Enterprises, Inc.
P.O. Box 547
Rye, NY 10580
(914) 967–1656

	Sea Hawk	Sweet Sue
Length	9 ft. 6 in.	10 ft.
Beam	4 ft. 1 in.	4 ft. 3 in.
Depth	2 ft.	2 ft.
Capacity	375 lb.	450 lb.
Weight	100 lb.	125 lb.
Max. hp	2	4
Rig	marconi	marconi
	42 sq. ft.	42 sq. ft.(m) 20 sq.ft.(j)
Price		
(row/sail)	$609/$989	$989/$1,499

Construction: Fiberglass construction that involves both chopped matt and hand-laid 24-ounce woven roving. Fittings are backed by hardwood blocks glassed in place. Sweet Sue has wooden gunwales (the others are flanged) and is built of Coremat, a nonwoven fiberglass material that offers excellent strength.

Comments: Ensign builds several other dinghy models, including catamaran types, in addition to those listed here. The boats are priced toward the lower end of the market. Designer/builder Mike Dapice has extensive experience in the small-boat business and a wide dealer network. Don't expect to get everything at these prices, but the boats have some nice touches and are covered by a two-year warranty.

———

Manufacturer: Edey & Duff, Ltd.
128 Aucoot Road
Mattapoisett, MA 02739
(617) 758–2743

	7 Foot	8 Foot	9 Foot
Length	7 ft.	8 ft.	9 ft.
Beam	4 ft.	4 ft. 3 in.	4 ft. 6 in.
Weight (w/o rig)	70 lb.	80 lb.	95 lb.
Capacity	500 lb.	750 lb.	850 lb.
Rig	marconi	marconi	marconi
	40 sq. ft.	50 sq. ft.	60 sq. ft.
Designer	Lyle Hess's Fatty Knees design		
Price	$1,400/$1,970	$1,500/$2,170	$1,650/$2,450

Construction: Hand-laid-up fiberglass, lapstrake with 20 stringers. A chopper gun is used to spray in the first layer of matt, which is then rolled out by hand. Additional material is used in the sheer and bottom. Then a layer of 1½-ounce matt is laid in, followed by a layer of 6-ounce cloth—all done consecutively to ensure a thorough bonding. Seats are laid up of matt and cloth and bonded with wide reinforcing strips. The interior is finished in gelcoat. The rails are built of steam-bent teak fastened with copper rivets, an excellent method.

Comments: A comparatively beamy dinghy (cartoppers may need a custom roofrack for the larger models) with high freeboard, the Fatty Knees offers excellent carrying capacity, is a good performer when being rowed, and is a notably good sailboat. Its lapstrake construction combines strength with reasonably light weight. Those ordering the sailing model should seriously consider the optional kick-up rudder. This is a well-designed, well-built, not-inexpensive dinghy that is especially noteworthy for those who will sail regularly or who are serious cruisers.

Manufacturer: Great Lakes Boat Building Co.
227 Prospect
South Haven, MI 49090
(616) 637–6805

Superior Dinghy	
Length	7 ft. 6 in.
Beam	3 ft. 8 in.
Weight	45 lb.
Designer	Design appeared in *Rudder* magazine in 1945.
Builder	Michael Kiefer
Price	approx. $1,500 (boats may be purchased as kits or bare hulls)

Construction: Bruynzeel marine plywood/epoxy with silicon-bronze fasteners. A breasthook and stern knees are fitted. Two sets of oarlock sockets are mounted. The bottom is protected by strakes.

Comments: This soft-chine dinghy is a handsome-looking boat that is notably lightweight. No sailing rig is fitted, the builder noting quite rightly

that few tiny boats sail very well and their daggerboard trunks add weight and clutter. Michael Kiefer builds only a few boats each year and guarantees the materials and workmanship for five years. This is an interesting dinghy.

Manufacturer: Halcyon Boats
  6011 Orange View Drive
  West Melbourne, FL 32904
  (305) 676–5425

	7-Foot Dinghy	9-Foot Dinghy
Length	7 ft.	9 ft.
Beam	3 ft. 8 in.	3 ft. 10 in.
Weight (approx.)	90 lb.	110 lb.
Rig	marconi, 27 sq. ft.	marconi, 38 sq. ft.
Design	9-foot hull based on 1880s hull used on the River Thames	
Price (row/sail)	$990/$1,700	$1,200/$1,950

Construction: Gelcoat followed by a layer of matt and a layer of roving with extra matt around the hull flanges, seats, and so forth. Hull is lapstrake. A hull liner enclosing foam flotation is used. The gunwale is a U-shaped flange—likely to represent an improvement over the more typical inverted-L flange design—and the oarlocks are set into wooden blocks within the flange. This dinghy is equipped with a standard stainless steel strip to protect its keel, and a bilge drain. A gunwale guard of aluminum with an inset rubber strip is available.

Comments: A reasonably good-looking dinghy with some excellent construction features. One of the 9-footers was sailed 90 miles across the Gulf Stream from Florida to the Bahamas, a passage recounted in *Small Boat Journal* in October 1980.

Manufacturer: Johannsen Boat Works
P.O. Box 570097
Miami, FL 33257-0097
(305) 445-7534

	Trinka 8	Trinka 10
Length	8 ft.	10 ft.
Beam	3 ft. 9 in.	4 ft. 2 in.
Weight (row/sail)	90/120 lb.	110/130 lb.
Capacity	650 lb.	1,000 lb.
Max. hp	2	4
Rig	marconi, 38 sq. ft.	marconi, 64 sq. ft.
Designer	Bruce Bingham	
Price (row/sail)	$1,345/$1,750	$1,650/$2,400

Construction: Hand-laid fiberglass with laminated teak inwales/outwales, teak breasthook and quarter knees. Four half-inch bronze oarlock sockets are fitted. A stainless steel half-oval is an option for the bow and a 1/8-inch stainless skeg shoe is also available, as are oak bottom skids and a stainless transom molding to protect the transom from damage by an anchor and chain.

Comments: A beautifully shaped dinghy, the Trinka has a somewhat higher freeboard than most, enhancing carrying capacity. The trade-off for the boat's sturdy construction is somewhat heavier weight than dinghies of similar length. Rowing is practical from the bow seat. This boat was designed by an experienced cruising sailor and offers exceptional features at a (currently) not-outrageous price.

Manufacturer: Lee Fiberglass Products
  P.O. Box 149
  Winthrop, ME 04364
  (207) 395–4797

Bufflehead	
Length	10 ft.
Beam	4 ft.
Depth	NA
Weight	115 lb.
Rig	marconi, 38 sq. ft.
Price	$650 (row)

Construction: Fiberglass with flanged gunwale and varnished mahogany seats.

Comments: Low-cost fiberglass boats.

Manufacturer: Lee's Workshop
  11907 Cedar Lane
  Kingsville, MD 21087
  (301) 592–6673

	Oxford Dinghy 8 1/2	Oxford Dinghy 10
Length	8 ft. 6 in.	10 ft.
Beam	4 ft. 5 in.	4 ft. 9 in.
Depth	1 ft. 6 in.	1 ft. 7 in.
Weight	115 lb.	135 lb.
Rig	sliding gunter	sliding gunter
	45 sq. ft.	62 sq. ft.
Designer	Dale Denning	
Price	$1,890	$2,150

Construction: Hand-laid fiberglass, mahogany gunwales, bronze hardware, and wood backing for towing eye. The floor has a nonskid finish.

Comments: This unusual dinghy has a rounded stern: The designer aimed at "closing" the water behind the boat in addition to easing the passage of the bow through the water. The Oxford Dinghy rows well and has two very

usable sets of oarlocks. Compared to other boats in its size range, the Oxford Dinghy is beamy. It is also roomy and very stable. These dinghies come with rigs that are relatively easy to raise and lower underway, something that cannot be said for many small dinghies. A clever, lever-action centerboard is used, rather than a daggerboard, so there is no daggerboard slot to admit water, and no daggerboard to lose or break. Not a lightweight, the Oxford Dinghy is a lovely boat of successful design. Its price is attractive, too.

Manufacturer: Longfield Dory Co.
 East Blue Hill, ME 04629
 (207) 374–5656

	Longfield Dinghy
Length	10 ft. 4 in.
Beam	4 ft. 2 in.
Weight	
(row/sail)	135/195 lb.
Rig	sliding gunter, 65 sq. ft.
Price	
(row/sail)	$1,200/$2,400

Construction: Hand-laid fiberglass with teak rails and thwarts. A stainless steel keel guard is standard.

Comments: A very pretty boat. It has longitudinal flotation tanks and storage for oars beneath the thwarts. A single set of oarlock sockets is provided.

Manufacturer: James W. Lynch
Indian Point Road
Mount Desert, ME 04660
(207) 288–5258

Lynch Dinghy	
Length	12 ft.
Beam	4 ft. 2 in.
Depth	1 ft. 6 in.
Weight	160 lb. (approx.)
Rig	lug, 70 sq. ft.
Designer	James W. Lynch
Price	NA

Construction: Hand lay-up of gelcoat followed by 1½-ounce matt, 18-ounce roving, 1½-ounce matt, 10-ounce cloth. The keel is built up with additional matt, and the keel/skeg area is filled with putty and covered with matt and cloth. Mahogany gunwales through-bolted with silicon-bronze bolts are typical, and the gunwales and oarlock sockets are bedded in epoxy and gap-filling microballoons. The oarlock sockets are through-bolted and have a backing plate. A thick wooden breasthook, hollowed on its underside to provide a convenient handhold, and stern knees are provided. The woodwork is treated with WEST System epoxy and Awlgrip. Hardware is bronze, purchased from Dyer.

Comments: This must be rated an exceptional dinghy built by a very experienced craftsman and sailor. It is a big, rugged dinghy that rows very well. Sailing models are fitted with centerboards and a sensible, salty-looking lug rig. If you can store a boat this size, the Lynch dinghy is a must-see.

Manufacturer: Newman Marine
  Box 20, Main Street
  Southwest Harbor, ME 04679
  (207) 244–3860

Newman Yacht Tender	
Length	11 ft. 9 in.
Beam	4 ft. 2 in.
Weight (w/o rig)	135 lb.
Rig	gaff, 54 sq. ft.
Designer	Arthur Spurling w/modifications for fiberglass construction
Price	$1,895/$2,695

Construction: Hand-laid-up fiberglass with teak trim. A wide keel is molded into the boat's bottom. Sailing models are fitted with an aluminum centerboard.

Comments: First offered in 1967, more than 300 of these boats have been built. Their construction is of high quality, capable of absorbing enormous abuse. The thick keel protects the bottom. Two rowing positions are available and rowing performance is excellent: 7-foot oars are standard. The boat tows easily and sails well enough to double as a daysailer. This is among the few dinghies fitted with a centerboard and a cat rig. Comparatively large and heavy, this is an excellent tender for those who can leave the boat in the water and, when not towing, lift it aboard with the aid of davits or tackle.

Manufacturer: Nordic Dinghy Co.
  2635—175th Avenue NE
  Redmond, WA 98052
  (206) 881–2622

	Nordic IX	**Nordic XI**
Length	9 ft.	11 ft.
Beam	4 ft. 3 in.	4 ft. 6 in.
Weight		
(row/sail)	110/145 lb.	165/200 lb.
Rig	marconi	gaff
	52 sq. ft.	72 sq. ft.
Designer	based on Scandinavian working small craft	
Price		
(row/sail)	$1,295/$1,795	$1,395/$2,095

Construction: Hand-laid-up lapstrake fiberglass with teak gunwales and trim. The IX has flotation enclosed below the thwarts, the XI in longitudinal tanks.

Comments: These are round-bottomed dinghies with full-length keels that should help them track in a straight line. Oak rubstrakes and a metal keel shoe are noteworthy options, as is a kick-up rudder, which should be considered necessary. The bow seat is not intended for rowing, so a single set of oarlocks is provided. Nordic dinghies appeal to those who like their "old-world" look. I suspect the IX represents the most practical model for use as a tender.

Manufacturer: North Shore Associates
  P.O. Box 78
  Anderson Road
  North Sebago, ME 04029
  (207) 787–3880

	Down-Easter 8	**Down-Easter 10**	**Down-Easter 12**
Length	8 ft. 5 in.	9 ft. 5 in.	11 ft. 5 in.
Beam	3 ft. 8 in.	3 ft. 11 in.	4 ft.
Depth	1 ft. 7 in.	1 ft. 7 in.	1 ft. 7 in.
Weight			
(row/sail)	90/100 lb.	100/110 lb.	130/145 lb.
Rig	marconi	marconi	marconi sloop
	38 sq. ft.	42 sq. ft.	71 sq. ft.
Designer	Mo Russo, Jr.		
Price			
(row/sail)	$759/$1,399	$1,599/$2,399	$1,899/$2,699

Construction: Boats are hand-laid fiberglass. Bronze and stainless fittings are used, and a brass rub strip is a useful option.

Comments: These are handsome-looking boats. The 10 and 12 are patterned after old wooden pulling boats. Only a single set of oarlocks is provided on the 8-footer. "North Shore" 10-foot and 12-foot models are also available, with substantially more wood and a generally more "yachtlike" appearance. The sailing version of the North Shore 12 has a lug rig. Check with builder for prices and delivery times. An 8-foot pram is also available. Kick-up rudders should be considered mandatory options.

Manufacturer: Rivendell Marine
   125 Lagoon Road
   Bend Boat Basin
   Melville, RI 02840
   (401) 683–1107

Columbia	
Length	11 ft. 6 in.
Beam	4 ft. 2 in.
Weight	130 lb.
Rig	Leg-o'-mutton/sprit
	63 sq. ft.
Designer	Nathanael Herreshoff
Price	
(row/sail)	$5,250/$6,000

Construction: These boats are built of white-cedar planking over white-oak keels and frames. Copper rivets and silicon-bronze fasteners are used.

Comments: Rivendell proprietor Tom Wolstenholme and some expert boatwrights have been building dinghies, and restoring/repairing larger boats, for more than a decade. The craftsmanship of this shop is exquisite and the three dinghies now offered cover a wide range of potential needs.

Manufacturer: RKL Boatworks
   Mount Desert, ME 04660
   (207) 244–5997 (day)
   (207) 244–3706 (night)

Lawley Tender	
Length	11 ft.
Beam	4 ft.
Depth	1 ft. 7 in.

Capacity	475 lb.
Weight	wd, 95 lb.
	f/g, 140 lb.
Rig	marconi
	30 sq. ft.
	2-pc. wood mast
Designer	George Lawley
Price	f/g row/sail $2,050/$3,400
	wd row/sail $4,500/$6,000

Construction: The Lawley is available in either fiberglass—hand lay-up with 1-ounce matt, 10-ounce cloth, 1-ounce matt—with teak trim and optional mahogany-plywood floorboards, or strip-planked, WEST System construction. The fiberglass Lawley has inner and outer wooden gunwales. Builder Bob Lincoln protects his cold-molded hulls with clear Awlgrip, rather than merely varnishing over the epoxy. A brass keel band is standard on wooden boats, optional on the fiberglass models. (RKL also offers several other boats, including a Rangeley design.)

Comments: Bob Lincoln has steadfastly and patiently carved out a business for himself, building and selling small craft. The craftsmanship is excellent. The Classic Lawley tender, with its tucked-up wineglass transom well out of the water, should combine excellent rowing and sailing performance. It also has a comparatively high freeboard, enhancing seaworthiness. Several East Coast dealers and one in the Midwest handle the boats, as does L.L. Bean (Rangeley models). Contact the builder for more details. These boats are worth investigating for anyone able to spend this sort of money.

Manufacturer: Robinhood Marine Center
  Robinhood, ME 04350
  (207) 371–2525

10-Foot Dinghy	
Length	10 ft. 6 in.
Beam	4 ft. 1 in.
Weight	175 lb.
Max. hp	2
Rig	sliding gunter, 65 sq. ft.
Designer	Cape Dory Yachts
Price (row/sail)	$2,095/$2,595

Construction: Hand-laid-up fiberglass with teak rails, thwarts, and transom. Bronze hardware.

Comments: Originally built by Cape Dory, which produced some 2,200 examples beginning in 1970, this dinghy has a Whitehall look and is rather lavishly trimmed with wood, contributing to her weight. The boats are well finished, and two sets of oarlock sockets are standard. A canvas gunwale guard is a $220 option. These boats row well but are tender.

Manufacturer: N.L. Silva & Co.
   7980 Market Street
   Wilmington, NC 28405
   (919) 686–4356

	Teal	Tern	Gull
Length	8 ft.	10 ft. 1 in.	11 ft. 5 in.
Beam	4 ft.	4 ft.	4 ft.
Capacity	400 lb.	500 lb.	700 lb.
Weight			
(row/sail)	80/85 lb.	90/100 lb.	100/125 lb.
Max. hp.	1.5	1.5	2
Rig	sprit	sprit	sprit
	40 sq. ft.	47 sq. ft.	48 sq. ft.
Designer	based on Whitehall boats		

Construction: Hand-laid-up fiberglass with mahogany gunwales and breasthook (through which the spruce mast is stepped) and quarter knees. Bronze oarlocks, one set, and a stainless towing eye with a backing plate.

Comments: These are very pretty boats. Gunwale protection appears modest at the pointed breasthook and there appears to be no provision for rowing from the bow seat. These are semicustom boats, however, and the builder would almost certainly entertain requests for specific detail changes.

Manufacturer: Starwing
  500 Wood Street
  P.O. Box 137
  Bristol, RI 02809
  (401) 254–0670

	First Mate	Navigator
Length	8 ft. 1 in.	9 ft. 5 in.
Beam	4 ft. 2 in.	4 ft. 2 in.
Weight	85 lb.	98 lb.
Capacity	475 lb.	555 lb.
Rig	rowing only	marconi main 42 sq. ft., jib 21 sq. ft.
Price (row/sail)	$649	$759/$1,379

Construction: Fiberglass construction that combines chopped matt with a layer of woven roving laid in by hand, and woven roving reinforcement in the flanged gunwale for extra rigidity. An exclusive rubrail, which the builder claims is particularly durable, is installed. It is a soft vinyl that is heated and stretched over the hull flange. Nice touches include a PVC shoe bonded to the skeg with epoxy. A repair kit is available to replace the PVC strip, but this must be done before the gelcoat is abraded away. Nonskid interior surfaces, a large bow seat, and two sets of bronze oarlocks. The 8-foot Harpooner model has a hull liner.

Comments: These are nice-looking and neatly finished dinghies, moderate in price. The rubrail is an interesting touch, as is the effort to provide a bow rowing position, useful when the dinghy is fully loaded with people and gear. Long term, some support for the teak center thwart might well be a plus.

Manufacturer: Winterport Boat Co.
  RFD #2, Box 810, Oak Street
  Winterport, ME 04496
  (207) 223–4882

Puffin	
Length	8 ft. 6 in.
Beam	49 in.
Weight	85 lb.
Max. hp	3
Rig	marconi, 39 sq. ft.
Designer	Dale C. Cottrell
Price	
(row/sail)	$595/$1,099

Construction: Hand-laid-up hull of matt and roving with oak gunwales and center thwart. The thwart is supported by an upright in its middle to resist bending. The oarlocks and bow eye are bronze, and the bow eye has a hardwood backing. The sailing model has spruce spars.

Comments: A nicely finished round-bottomed dinghy with wooden gunwales attached with screws. It is reasonably lightweight for its size. A second set of oarlocks would be a plus, as would a sculling notch and wooden motor-mount pad.

Manufacturer: Yankee Boat Works
   P.O. Box 670
   21 Rockland Place
   Stamford, CT 06904
   (203) 348–4049

	Liberty	**Heritage**
Length	9 ft. 6 in.	10 ft.
Beam	3 ft. 7 in.	4 ft. 3 in.
Depth	1 ft. 7 in.	2 ft.
Weight	75 lb.	125 lb.
Max. hp	2	2
Rig	gaff, 60 sq. ft.	
Price	check with builder	

Construction: Hand-laid-up "lapstrake" fiberglass with wooden gunwales. Two sets of oarlock sockets are provided on the Liberty.

PLANS AND KITS

Plans: John Atkin
   P.O. Box 3005
   Noroton, CT 06820
   (203) 655–0886

	Cabin Boy	**Schatze**	**Flipper**
Length	7 ft. 6 in.	7 ft. 10 in.	10 ft.
Beam	3 ft. 10 in.	3 ft. 7½ in.	3 ft. 11½ in.
Rig	sprit		marconi
	36 sq. ft.		55 sq. ft. (one set of reefs)
Designer	John Atkin		
Price	check with designer		

Construction: Lapstrake wood. Plywood can be used for frames, planks, and bottoms (preferably Bruynzeel here).

Comments: Cabin Boy and Flipper are flat-bottomed skiffs; Schatze is a flat-bottomed pram. According to the designer, there should be little difference in drag when towing Cabin Boy or Flipper, and Flipper might tow a straighter line because the beam-to-length ratio is improved. Cabin Boy and Schatze have fore-and-aft rowing thwarts and two sets of oarlock sockets. The boats have good-sized skegs, adequately proportioned rudders, and, for simplicity, daggerboards. Cabin Boy's spars stow within the hull. These are *all* nice small boats, and other dinghy plans are available. More than 100 Cabin Boy plans have been sold; its construction was described in the now-out-of-print *Building the Skiff Cabin Boy* by Clemens C. Kuhlig. The designer can be relied on for advice and counsel during your project. Of Cabin Boy, the designer reports: "In all due respect, she is too fat. On the other hand, that spells capacity and that, apparently, is what many people want. Despite her ample beam, she rows well and sails in a satisfactory manner for such a little boat." Cabin Boy is pictured in Chapter 2.

Plans: The Back 'n Forth Co.
42 Gann Road
East Hampton, NY 11937
(516) 324–6393

	Uqbar 6	Uqbar 7	Uqbar 8	Uqbar 10
Length	5 ft. 11 in.	6 ft. 10 in.	7 ft. 10 in.	9 ft. 10 in.
Beam	3 ft. 10 in.	4 ft.	4 ft.	4 ft. 9 in.
Capacity	2 adults	2 adults +	3 adults +	4 adults +
Weight	35 lb.	42 lb.	55 lb.	72 lb.
Rig		sprit	sprit	sprit
		32 sq. ft.	32 sq. ft.	55 sq. ft.
Designer	Redjeb Jordania			
Price (kit)$249	$269		$289	$389
	(sailing versions add $225-$345)			

For a complete description, see the Pram section.

Plans: B & B Yacht Designs
P.O. Box 206, Elm Stret
Vandemere, NC 28587
(919) 745–4793

Catspaw	
Length	7 ft. 10½ in.
Beam	4 ft. 6 in.
Weight	60 to 70 lb.
Rig	sprit or marconi/36 sq. ft.
Designer	Graham S. Byrnes, N.A.
Price	$35

Construction: The Catspaw is designed for "stitch-and-glue" sheet-plywood construction.

Comments: The Catspaw is a family of prams ranging from the 6½-foot Minipaw to a 9-foot model. (A nesting dinghy, the Twopaw, and the stem-bowed Spindrift models are also available.) The plans of the Catspaw dinghies suggest these are *very* well-designed tenders. The bottom is protected by rub strips. The hull is reinforced by quarter knees fore and aft. Two sets of rowlocks are shown. The boats have ample freeboard and look good.

Plans: Baker Boat Works
  29 Drift Road
  Westport, MA 02790
  (508) 636–5576

	Puddleduck	Gosling	Tern	Swallow	North Shore
Length	7 ft. 10 in.	9 ft. 6 in.	10 ft.	10 ft. 7 in.	11 ft.
Beam	4 ft.	4 ft. 3 in.	4 ft. 7 in.	3 ft. 9¾ in.	4 ft. 9¾ in.
Price	approx. $27 to $36				

Construction: Puddleduck is plywood. Gosling is wood carvel or fiberglass. Tern is plywood or fiberglass. Swallow is carvel. North Shore Dinghy is lapstrake.

Comments: Designed by Robert Baker (Swallow is attributed to N. Herreshoff but Baker took off the lines), these are all good-looking boats of varying degrees of difficulty, as noted in the catalog. There are several skiffs, particularly the 11-foot model (plan 71) designed by Fred Tripp, that might also make very suitable tenders.

Plans/Kits: Bardon Inc.
  P.O. Box 15243
  Des Moines, IA 50315

	Deck-Dink
Length	8 ft.
Beam	4 ft.
Depth	1 ft. 7 in.
Weight	95 lb.
Capacity (lb./people)	425/2
Max. hp	3½

Dimensions	
(stowed)	4 ft. x 4½ ft.
Designer	Don Hagge
Price	plans $25/kit $219

Construction: Plywood, epoxy.

Comments: The designer notes the boat's latching system makes it quick and easy to join the halves.

Plans: Dave Gerr
420 East 79th Street
New York, NY 10021
(212) 570–6750

Pippin	
Length	11 ft.
Beam	4 ft. 3 in.
Weight	120 lb.
Capacity	600 lb. (approx.)
Rig	sprit, 64 sq. ft.
Designer	Dave Gerr

Construction: Wood/epoxy construction of marine plywood, ash, mahogany, and oak with Sitka spruce spars. Bronze hardware. A centerboard is fitted.

Comments: Patterned after garvey workboats still popular on Barnegat Bay and other bodies of shallow water, Pippin is a sophisticated pram. The boat offers a *lot* of room throughout her length. Her flat bottom makes this boat exceptionally stable, and the designer claims that one can step on her rail (which, of course, you wouldn't do!) without fear of swamping or capsizing. The loose-footed spritsail appears to have an adequate sheet arrangement. This sailing garvey would make excellent shore-to-ship transportation and serve as a general fun boat that is trailerable. One might question whether Pippin would tow well, but owners of cruising boats large enough to carry her on deck or in davits might well consider her. Epoxy-coated plywood boats, if well built, do not offer significant maintenance problems.

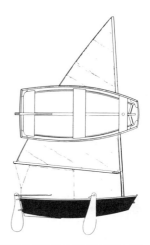

Plans/Kits: Ken Hankinson Associates
  P.O. Box 2551
  La Habra, CA 90631
  (213) 947–1241

Sabotina	
Length	7 ft. 10 in.
Beam	3 ft. 11 in.
Depth	1 ft. 3 in.
Weight	50 lb.
Max. hp	3
Rig	marconi, 34 to 38 sq. ft.
Designer	Ken Hankinson
Price	plans $33/kit, approx. $279 (plus $215 for rig)

Construction: Plywood, stitch-and-glue.

Comments: An easily built, V-bottomed pram. The sailing version is equipped with a leeboard.

Manufacturer: Merryman Boats (kits)
127 West North Street
Ithaca, MI 48847
(517) 875–3788

	Tadpole	Frog
Length	6 ft.	7 ft. 10 in.
Beam	3 ft.	4 ft.
Depth	1 ft. 6 in.	1 ft. 10 in.
Max. hp	2	4
Weight	45 lb.	72 lb.
Rig	gaff, 30 sq. ft.	sprit w/jib, 40 sq. ft.
Designer	Merryman Boats	
Price	$599	N/A

Construction: Marine plywood/epoxy—all parts precut.

Comments: A wheel is built into the bow and handles are attached to the transom, simplifying the task of getting the boat to the water. A color-coded manual and some tools are included in the kit. The quality of photos makes it hard to judge aspects of the design in terms of its use as a tender, but the idea of these boats is intriguing, and Merryman is worth a call if you are considering a kit.

Plans: Kennedy Osborne
   1555 West Coral Court
   Merritt Island, FL 32952

	Hummingbird
Length	7 ft. 10 in.
Beam	3 ft. 11½ in.
Weight	64 lb.
Capacity	385 lb.
Rig	marconi, 38 sq. ft.
Designer	Kennedy Osborne
Price	$22

Construction: Stitch-and-glue plywood.

Comments: A pram with adequate-looking rocker that was designed by a live-aboard cruiser.

Plans: Harold H. Payson & Co.
   Pleasant Beach Road
   South Thomaston, ME 04858
   (207) 594–7587

	Nymph	**Tortoise**
Length	7 ft. 9 in.	6 ft. 5 in.
Beam	3 ft. 6 in.	3 ft. 2 in.
Designer	Phil Bolger	Phil Bolger
Price	$20	$20

Construction: Plywood—Payson recommends AC—tack-and-tape.

Comments: Both these boats are economical and easy to build. Nymph is a particularly handsome double-chine pram. Tortoise represents perhaps the least expensive, yet practical, tender one can build. Nineteen plans are currently available from Payson for Bolger-designed "instant boats." Payson's books on the building of simple plywood boats are must reading for the home builder or small-craft enthusiast. Tortoise was described in *Small Boat Journal,* August 1979 (Vol. 1, No. 1), Nymph in *Small Boat Journal,* September 1985 (Number 44).

Plans: Raycon Marine Services
202 S. W. 192d Street
Seattle, WA 98166

Rebel 9	
Length	9 ft.
Beam	4 ft.
Weight	100 lb.
Max. hp	2.5
Rig	gunter/45 sq. ft.
Designer	Raymond Connell
Price	$40 ($2 for brochure)

Construction: Cold-molded.

Comments: The Rebel series also includes 8- and 10-foot models. These are soft-chine boats.

Kits: Shell Boats
  RD 3, Box 255A
  St. Albans, VT 05748
  (802) 524–9645

	Sea Shell 8	Sea Shell 10
Length	7 ft. 10 in.	10 ft.
Beam	4 ft. 2 in.	5 ft. 3 in.
Weight	65 lb.	90 lb.
Max. hp	2	5
Rig	marconi w/sprit boom	marconi w/sprit boom
	35 sq. ft.	50 sq. ft.
Designer	Fred Shell	
Price	$875 (rig adds $420)	$1,100 (rig adds $550)

Construction: Glued, lapstrake marine plywood with epoxy coating. Spruce or pine frames, bronze hardware and fastenings.

Comments: Interesting-looking prams of a rather Scandinavian appearance, these boats may have some appeal as both all-around fun boats and yacht tenders.

Plans: Sponberg Yacht Design
  P.O. Box 661
  Newport, RI 02840
  (401) 849–5661

	Halfling	Chula
Length	7 ft. 10 in.	9 ft. 1 in.
Beam	4 ft.	3 ft. 4 in.

Weight	80 lb.	100 lb.
Capacity	800 lb.	500 lb.
Rig	marconi, 37 sq. ft.	sprit, 32 sq. ft.
Designer	Eric W. Sponberg, N.A.	
Price	$35	$35

Construction: Halfling is for plywood (estimated materials cost $300 to $500), Chula is for either plywood or foam-cored fiberglass (estimated materials cost $500 to $700).

Comments: Halfling is a pram design, and can be built as a nesting dinghy to save space aboard. It has a generous weight-carrying capacity. Chula is a double-chine, V-bottomed boat that can be expected to be somewhat tender initially, compared to Halfling, while offering good performance. The designer will supply advice as needed.

Plans: Tangent Development Co.
   1715 Harlequin Run
   Austin, TX 78758
   (512) 837–9170

Dory Dinghy	
Length	11 ft. 2 in.
Beam	3 ft. 10 in.
Weight	75 lb. (rig adds 24 lb.)
Capacity (lb./people)	450/3
Rig	sprit, 36 sq. ft.
Designer	J.G. Merritt
Price	$15

Construction: Plywood over fir frames.

Comments: Decked at either end to provide storage space and protection for

foam flotation, as well as to keep the water out when launching, the Dory Dinghy might interest some home builders looking for a larger tender. A leeboard is used for sailing. The plans and instructions are quite complete and include a recommended list of tools.

Plans: Charles Wittholz
   100 Williamsburg Drive
   Silver Spring, MD 20901
   (301) 593-7711

Catboat Dinghy	
Length	11 ft.
Beam	5 ft.
Weight	175 lb.
Rig	gaff, 80 sq. ft.
Designer	Charles Wittholz
Price	$25 (add $10 for full-size body plan)

Construction: This boat was designed for cold-molded construction. A daggerboard is used.

Comments: Intended primarily for those who can stow a dinghy aboard, the Catboat Dinghy is a miniature Cape Cod catboat but with the fine bow and stern of a Whitehall-type rowing boat. Several have been built, and the designer can share with you reports on their performance.

Plans: Bernard L. Wolfard
Commonsense Designs
2801 Whitney Avenue
Baltimore, MD 21215
(301) 367–1982

Brick	
Length	8 ft.
Beam	4 ft.
Depth	2 ft.
Weight	approx. 70 lb.
Capacity	475 to 875(!) lb.
Max. hp	2.5
Rig	off center marconi, w/sprit boom
	59 sq. ft.
Price	$20

Construction: Three sheets of ¼-inch 4- by 8-foot plywood. Takes one day to build.

Comments: Utterly simple and, according to Wolfard, utterly useful. Sailing version uses a leeboard. An apparently improbable boat that would make an entirely satisfactory dinghy for a great many home builders.

Plans/Kits: WoodenBoat Magazine
P.O. Box 78
Brooklin, ME 04616
(207) 359–4652

Nutshell	
Length	7 ft. 7 in.
Beam	4 ft.
Weight	90 lb.
Rig	lug, 57 sq. ft.
Designer	Joel White
Price	plans $75/kit (row/sail) $650/$800
	(add $145 for sail)

Construction: Lapstrake plywood.

Comments: This is a robust pram with a well-rockered flat bottom, two practical rowing stations, and a sensible rig. The magazine offers a video that covers the boat's construction. Plans for a 9-foot 6-inch version are also available, as are plans and "how-to" booklets for several other tenders of varying degrees of difficulty.

Further Reading

Bits and pieces of dinghy lore and advice appear in a great many books and magazines. The following list represents only a portion, but each item on the list is worth your time. Although some of the books are out of print, they may be available through your library or from one of the specialists in used boating books.

Books

Bingham, Bruce, *The Sailor's Sketchbook* (Seven Seas Press, Camden, Maine). Contains useful sketches and thoughts on off-shore towing and rigging a boat boom.

Bolger, Philip C., *Small Boats* (International Marine, Camden, Maine). An interesting book by one of today's most original and thought-provoking designers.

Bolger, Philip C., *100 Small Boat Rigs* (International Marine, Camden, Maine). Discusses various rigs, if not their hardware; of interest to anyone contemplating a sailing dinghy.

Childers, Erskine, *The Riddle of the Sands* (Dover Publications, Inc., New York). An adventure/spy novel imbued with salt air and the reality of small-boat sailing. Excellent material on the level of seamanship that can be practiced aboard a dinghy.

Coote, Jack H., *Total Loss* (Sheridan House, Dobbs Ferry, NY). A book of very scary tales about lost boats. Dinghies figure prominently in these stories of misfortune.

Everitt, Dick, and Witt, Roger, *This is Boat Handling at Close Quarters* (Hearst Marine Books, New York). Includes several pages of wonderfully simple illustrations and concise advice about dinghy improvements and handling.

Herreshoff, L. Francis, *The Compleat Cruiser* (Sheridan House, Dobbs Ferry, New York). Proper boat handling and seamanship presented in story fashion by the great designer. The dinghy is not neglected.

Pardey, Lin and Larry, *The Capable Cruiser* (W.W. Norton, New York). Contains a good chapter on tenders and the views of this engaging and experienced cruising couple.

Payson, Harold H., *Instant Boats* (International Marine, Camden, Maine). All about building simple boats of plywood. This and Payson's other books are must reading for the amateur builder.

Roth, Hal, *After 50,000 Miles* (W.W. Norton, New York). The dinghy as viewed by a long-distance cruiser.

Smith, Hervey Garrett, *The Arts of the Sailor* (D. Van Nostrand Company, Inc., New York). Explanations and sketches of knots, splices, whippings, etc., that will be as useful for the dinghy-owner as the big boat skipper.

Steet, Don, *The Ocean Sailing Yacht* (W.W. Norton, New York). Strong opinions based on sound experience.

Magazines

Cruising World (Newport, Rhode Island). Among the sailing monthlies, *Cruising World* has given the most attention to dinghies. As with most boating publications, readers will not find *Consumer Reports*–type analysis here. But there are not-infrequent pieces on dinghy improvement and design.

WoodenBoat (Brooklin, Maine). Although the boats covered are of wood construction, the information about design and performance is relevant to fiberglass boats as well. Over the years, the magazine has published a great many worthwhile pieces on dinghies and sells several plans for excellent boats and a dinghy kit. Browse through back issues if you can.

Small Boat Journal (Bennington, Vermont). The smallest of small craft have played a surprisingly small role in this bimonthly. However, it was in SBJ that Phil Bolger's *Tortoise* design was published, and the news of new dinghies usually appears here.

Practical Sailor (Newport, Rhode Island). A subscription-only publication that evaluates and surveys gear and boats, *Practical Sailor* occasionally takes a brief look at dinghies.

Index

Photo Credits

All photographs by the author except as noted: front cover; top left by Starwing Inc.; bottom photo by Chris Cunningham; p. 18 top and p. 62, courtesy Lee's Workshop; p. 22 bottom, photo by Bob Hilton; p. 23, courtesy Pete Baker; p. 28, courtesy The Rockport Apprenticeshop; p. 31, p. 42 bottom, and p. 115, courtesy The Anchorage; p. 48 top, courtesy Grumman; p. 48 bottom and p. 61, courtesy Ensign Dinghies; p. 63, courtesy North Shore Yachts; p. 64 top, courtesy Eric Sponberg; p. 64 bottom, courtesy Jarvis Newman; p. 68 right, courtesy Spiffy Dink; p. 72, courtesy Bill Cannell; p. 76 right, courtesy Dick Janda; p. 80, courtesy OMC; p. 85 bottom, courtesy Avon; p. 85 top and pp. 87 and 88, courtesy Goodyear Tire and Rubber Co. All photographs in Chapter Seven are courtesy of the manufacturers.